WORKING MEN'S COLLEGE

LIBRARY REGULATIONS.

THE LIVING TIDE

THE LIVING TIDE

by

N. J. BERRILL

LONDON
VICTOR GOLLANCZ LTD
1951

Printed in Great Britain by
Lowe and Brydone Printers Limited, London, N.W.10

To my children MICHAEL, ELSILYN and PEGGY, and
above all to JACQUELYN, my wife

ACKNOWLEDGMENTS

Every author is inevitably indebted to many other people for assistance, great or small, tangible or otherwise. In particular I would like to express my indebtedness to Dr. Edward Weyer, Jr., editor of *Natural History* magazine, for constant encouragement, and to Wallace Pollock for technical photographic assistance; and in general to those naturalists before me who have recorded their impressions and studies of the life of the shallow seas.

TABLE OF CONTENTS

1	The Road to the Keys	1
2	Turtle Sands	7
3	The Birth and Death of an Island	19
4	The Reef and the Worm	25
5	The Moat	35
6	The Power and the Glory	45
7	Crabs and Sponges	54
8	The Sands of Time	65
9	The Sailor and the Cross	77
10	Sea Food	85
11	Pilgrim Shore	97
12	Maine Lobster	108
13	Sea Plague and Seaweed	116
14	The Rockland	122
15	Rockpools	139
16	The Miners	149
17	The Head of the Cove	157
18	Ageless Anemones	162
19	Scallops and a Dredge	172
20	Islands in Fog	176
21	Pacific Interlude	187
22	Submarine Rockets	195
23	Seals for Texas	214
24	Sea Harvest	223
25	The Sea in the City	242
	Index	247

ILLUSTRATIONS

Photographs follow Page 82

A Plumose anemone trapping small sea animals
A Plumose anemone spawning its eggs
Starfishes hunting on sponges
Moon-jellies and comb-jellies
The underside of a Crucifix fish skull
The Horseshoe crab and the Fiddler crab
A Hermit crab in the empty shell of a moon snail
Starfish raiding a bed of mussels
Squid swimming backwards
A cluster of Hydroids
Sand Dollars and Brittle-star
Queen Trigger fish
Hole in a clam shell drilled by a whelk
Whelk's rasping tooth-ribbon
Young lobster larva
Zoea larva of the shore crab
A stalk-eyed Octopus
A fish-eye view of a Sea Raven
Young Cormorants in their nest
A young Seal on a fish-hatchery boat
Cormorants nesting in dead trees

THE LIVING TIDE

THE ROAD TO THE KEYS

THE bus ambled out of Miami and picked up speed as the settlements to the south began to dwindle. The larger trees thinned out, and Florida Pines stood out sharply against the sky. Then they too were gone and the land flattened, and all was scrub. Wild lime ripened in the thickets and tenuous creeks fingered their way toward the road.

I was on my way to the Dry Tortugas. The year was 1938 and I wanted to visit the Carnegie Marine Laboratory there, on Loggerhead Key, before it was to close down—which it did permanently in 1940—and study the local warm-water fauna while the studying was still good.

I am a marine zoologist by profession. My own work is, and has always been, almost as lonely as the long road that was now taking me down the Keys—the investigation of the problems of development of eggs and animal buds and the dim beginnings of the vertebrate type of animal (of which Man is probably the most illustrious recent development) which I think lie somewhere in the trail of the Tunicates, seaborne animals which are a sub-branch of the Chordates, the vertebrates being another.

My trip to the Tortugas was by way of getting to know marine life for its own sake, a wonderful kind of busman's holiday on which I'd study whatever tunicates I found. But it was also in a sense the beginnings of a slow crawl up the Atlantic coast, as it will become apparent as our story unfolds, from the Tortugas to Maine, from warm water to cold, from a marine fauna which is tropical or subtropical to one that is essentially subarctic—from the source of the Gulf Stream, following its northward sweep until it leaves our shores for Europe, to be replaced in the Gulf of Maine by cold water coming down from the North. The Tortugas seemed a logical place to begin.

Suddenly the flat land we were crossing narrowed. The road ran out along a green bar and slowly rose toward the blue. The Overseas Highway was beginning and we were really on our way. Here the road turned into a white strip reaching into the sky and rose high on long bridges spanning water and reefs. Small, flat keys at the ends of these bridges were barely visible and the world was all air and water. The arching dome of blue rested on two broad pillars, the Atlantic Ocean on the east and the Gulf of Mexico on the west. Only this sea-going road, and it was man-made, had any substance. You knew it was there because the bus, you hoped, was traveling over it, you were in the bus, and the map and bus schedule were proof that the road would stop at Key West. Otherwise the whole thing might have gone indefinitely on across the Gulf to Yucatan and Central America.

Streaks and tongues of light green water intermingled with darker blue, sliding through the channels beneath the bridges. White coral beaches fringed each little key, and palms leaned over to drop coconuts at the edge of the bare sand. Mangrove grew everywhere and the white heron explored for crabs and fish among its roots. Then at last, as the sun lowered, the road lay on Key West and came to its sudden, announced end in the town itself.

Key West may be part of the continental United States, but it is only by virtue of the road that reaches down between two oceans and not at all by the grace of God. A tropical, sea-girt island where pirates once based and an old Spanish town now stands, its name has nothing to do with "West," but is a corruption of the Spanish "Cayo Hueso" or "Island of Bones." I went down to the dock to board my boat to the Tortugas. Brown pelicans rested on the mooring posts, green turtles paddled slowly in the turtle-pound awaiting market. A ship from Cuba unloaded ripe pineapples and the air was heavy with sweet scent. Havana itself lay just beyond the horizon to the south (a two-hour drive if our road had continued on past Key West) and between it and us lay the Tropic of Cancer.

It was too late to sail that day, for the tropical night falls quickly and the reefs are dangerous. But at dawn our vessel, the *Dohrn*, with a few bumps against the wharf and grunts from its engine, slid out among the anchored fishing boats and headed for our destination, some seventy miles to the west. The *Dohrn*, a sixty-foot craft used for the bi-weekly trip to Key West and for marine expeditions around the keys of the Tortugas and Marquesas, was named for Anton Dohrn, a German professor of zoology who built and operated the first and greatest marine biological laboratory of them all, the famous Naples Aquarium. He sniffed derisively at his later big imitators at Plymouth, England, and Woods Hole, Massachusetts. His son Richard is now in charge at Naples.

As we left Key West, strands of golden brown and yellow

B

gulf weed floated by in the blue-green water, starting their
journey through the Straits of Florida. I wondered how far
they would drift, for just beyond the shore counter-current
was the source of the Gulf Stream, the spout of the kettle, the
greatest river in the sea. Some of the weed would drift in
among the Bahamas, some would be carried with the Stream
to the north, to the Grand Banks of Newfoundland and beyond, and some would swing away from the eastern edge of
the Stream to enter the great, swirling eddy that is the Sargasso Sea. Here in the Straits where we lay, the Stream flowed
east at several knots, a current that flowed so strongly up the
Atlantic side of Florida that when Ponce de Leon tried to
sail south against it after his first landing at St. Augustine in
1513 his ship was carried back in spite of the aid of a strong
following wind.

The water flows through the narrow gap between Cuba
and the Keys at three and one-half knots, about as fast as you
can walk and faster than you can row a good boat. Whether
this is fast or slow to you depends on your temperament, but
the net outcome is one hundred billion tons of warm salt
water carried past the Florida Keys every hour and poured
into the Atlantic, as great a discharge as a thousand Missis-
sippis. Small wonder the Stream sweeps up the Atlantic coast
and across the ocean to soften the climate of Britain and
Scandinavia before its impetus is lost!

The day was dead calm, and water and sky got more dazzling as the sun rose higher. The only relief for me (after two
hours afloat I will gladly swap you a boat for an island any
time) was to look as straight down into the sea as possible.
Only once in a while a jellyfish went by, but gulfweed swirled

past at least once a minute. I wanted to fish some out for examination but the speed of the *Dohrn* would have bounced a
bucket or torn it out of my hand.

It was tantalizing for a naturalist, for this Sargasso weed is
an ancient one of warm seas, embodying a little world of its
own. Small bladders buoy it up and only the oldest fronds
sink. New branches grow continuously and this weed is unique
in propagating vigorously in the open ocean far away from
any land. Each tangled mass of it gives shade and protection,
from sun and enemies, to a host of small animals, many of
which are not known to live anywhere else. Little brown-and-
yellow flatworms and sea slugs spend all their lives creeping
along the branches. Some of the strands that slipped past the
hull of our boat surely contained one or two sea horses with
tails curled tightly around a narrow stem. If true, the fish
might make the hitch-hike as far north as Long Island, to drop
off into the Sound or along the edge of Martha's Vineyard to
try a new life among the eel grass.

The *Dorhn* slowed suddenly almost to a stop as we passed
close to the dangerous reefs of the Marquesas, one of the few
coral atolls outside the South Pacific. And now was the time
to swing a pail overside in front of a patch of weed. Some of
it caught and came aboard with the water.

No sea horse was among it, but there was another fish, and
one that belonged to the gulfweed in an even closer way—the
Sargasso fish itself. I had known about it for years but had
never seen one. It was the fishing frog, Pterophryne, a small,
grotesque relative of the large and ugly angler of northern
coasts. Smaller, perhaps, this little gargoyle nevertheless has
its own bizarre beauty. It clings to the weed with hand-like

pectoral fins, while bands and mottling of brown and yellow on its skin blend with the colors of its tangled home, and frond-like processes growing from its body perfect the camouflage.

The weed may have held other animals that could have washed away in the rush of water while I pulled it in. For no less than twelve species belong in it, all of them trade-marked with the gulf weed colors—four fish, two crabs, two shrimps, three snails and one flatworm. Their very existence alone points to the great antiquity of this ocean weed, for the fitting of their color and adjustment of their form to the Sargasso weed could have been no simple task for evolving nature and may well have taken millions of years. There is even an earthworm that lives only on tropical beaches beneath decaying masses of this tide-tossed gulfweed.

At last the Tortugas drew near, as streaks of green and yellow flashed in the water as we threaded between shoals, and the bastion formation of Fort Jefferson and finally Loggerhead Key with its lighthouse loomed up. The *Dohrn* circled to move slowly in toward the small wharf on the western beach of Loggerhead where the Carnegie Laboratory lay half hidden in the coconut palms and casuarinas that had been planted when it was built in 1900. The beach glared white under the intense sun, and the half-shade of the trees was welcome. I felt a little like a prisoner as I realized I couldn't get back to Key West even if I wanted, but evening came, the air cooled and sweetened, and the shade deepened. Then as dusk faded to dark night, the silence that only sea islands know slipped softly over the sands. My "busman's holiday" had begun.

CHAPTER TWO

TURTLE SANDS

THE sun rose, a pale, yellow fire gleaming through a bank of clouds lying low on the horizon, sending a thin shadow of palms down the western beach of Loggerhead Key. When I went out, the tide was low and the sand was hard near the water's edge. Walking here was easy, but it was like walking into a scene in a pastel drawing—no movement, no stirring of sea or wind, no sound, and little color, and the water so gently warm it was hard to tell whether you walked in or out of it.

Round the curve of the beach loomed the dark upper column of the Loggerhead Light, an exclamation mark on a coral strand, warning Gulf shipping that this shimmering world of light was more substantial than it seemed.

Suddenly in this otherwise lifeless and motionless world a trail of life and motion lay across my path—a broad track in the hard-packed sand led up to the softer sand which lay above the mark of high tide. At some time during the night a turtle had struggled out of the sea to lay her eggs and this was the mark of her returning. Up at the top of the trail the sand had clearly been disturbed by more than wind, and somewhere beneath its surface lay a hundred or more large white eggs.

To the zoologist, as to any adventurer, there is always a thrill at the unexpected discovery of life, and the sign of the sea turtle brought to my mind a queer mixture of glamorous and grotesque images of the tropics. But my feeling of surprise was also an indication of a tragedy. The finding of a turtle trail should *not* have been a surprise but a commonplace, for this was Loggerhead Key in the Dry Tortugas, so named by the English buccaneers and before them by Ponce de Leon himself for the Loggerhead turtles that came here to breed. Of all places on earth the sea turtle should be at home here, and each night should see them crawling by the dozen up the beaches to lay and bury their fragile eggs.

That time has long since gone. Turtle eggs and turtle soup are too much of a delicacy, and wherever man comes the turtle has little chance. The prospects even of this batch of eggs were poor, for they were buried almost at the foot of the lighthouse, and the keeper had too much time on his hands, too much of an inclination for turtle, and too much experience at hunting for them to last. If the eggs had been buried farther down the beach the salt water would have penetrated the limy but porous shells and the embryos would have drowned, for turtle eggs are things of the land and not the sea. Turtles know enough to ascend the beach beyond the reach of the tide—an ancient knowledge sunk deep into instinct and no longer a question of intelligent decision even if it ever had been. The breeding routine of a female turtle is as complex and as unchangeable a pattern of behavior as any in creation. It was here on this sandpatch of an island that the attempt was made to study it thirty or more years ago by Davenport Hooker and later by Dr. S. O. Mast.

I hoped the eggs would remain undiscovered, though there was nothing much to be done except keep away and call no further attention to the spot—then perhaps they would develop into baby sea turtles. Turtle eggs, which compare favorably, shell, yolk and albumen, with a hen's egg, hatch after six to eight weeks, depending on the average temperature of the enveloping sand. When its time comes, the shell that was a cradle may become a tomb, for a turtle's hatching is as difficult and hazardous a process as is a baby chick's. Yet it is after hatching has been successfully accomplished that the real troubles of life begin. First of all, the young turtles hatch in warm darkness beneath two feet of sand, and with little intelligence and no experience of life they must climb to the surface and head down the beach to the sea.

Young turtles climb upward in the dark, repulsed by the force of gravity, to emerge on top of the sand. It is an instinct of a very simple type, coming under the heading of "forced movements." Not to obey it, but to succumb instead to gravity's downward pull would mean permanent burial and death. Once on top and as soon as they sense the light, the climbing instinct seems to disappear, and they react to what can be seen, even though still without understanding. Some years ago, when the Loggerheads were commoner, a naturalist visiting the island was able to show that the emerging young move away from a broken horizon (land) toward an open one (sea), from green and orange light (foliage, sand and sun) toward the blue—involuntary actions that send them on their way down to the sea.

Apparently all newly hatched turtles look so much alike that experts cannot tell them apart, but whether Loggerhead, Hawksbill, Leatherback, or Green Turtle, their infant journey from the upper beach down to the ocean beyond the reefs is a dangerous gantlet that few survive. Sea birds and

crabs pick them off one by one. In the Pacific the frigate bird
assembles on the nesting grounds to feed on the hatchlings as
they emerge, and even the few that do succeed in reaching the
water's edge alive find hungry fish waiting to get them. Of
twelve hatchlings that were released at low water off Heron
Island in the Australian Barrier Reef and followed in their
journey through the water, not one survived. All were de-
voured by fish lurking among the coral.

The conspiracy applies to their elders as well. Turtles are
caught most easily at the time of their egg-laying. For whether
it is safe or not they must come ashore to make their nest in
the dry sand. In an old John Speed atlas with a map of the
Islands dated 1622, there is printed what is possibly the oldest
accurate account of sea turtle breeding, written by a surveyor
for the first Virginia Company. "Shortly after their first coming in," the account runs, "the male and female couple, which
we call cooting, this they continue some three daies together
during which time they will scarcely separate, though a boat
come to them, nor hardly when they are smitten. Not long
after the she-turtle comes up by night upon some sandy Bay;
and farther up than the water uses to flow: she digs a hole
with her finns in the sand some two foot deep; and there,
coming up several nights, lays her eggs, some half a bushel
(which are about as big as a hen's egg and round as a ball)
and each time covers them with sand very curiously; so that
no man shall hardly find the place. These eggs (as it seems)
are afterwards hatched by the heat of the sun, and then by
the Providence of God (the means as yet unknown to us) are
brought out of the earth; for we could never perceive that she

returns anymore to them, and yet in likelihood they remain not long in the earth after they are hatched."

The nest-making of the four common sea turtles has been closely watched by naturalists in both East Indies and West Indies, and the procedure differs only in small detail. All but the Loggerheads frequent the sandy beaches of Ceylon, and to that tropical island of enchantment the naturalist Deraniyagala vividly describes the return of the giant Leather-back: "Glistening silvery in the moonlight, the turtle ascended the beach in a straight line to the sandy embankment created by the scouring action of the waves. Through this obstacle she cut her path with simultaneous jerks of her powerful fore flippers and gained the dry sand. Here, she commenced what the Senegalese fishermen term a 'sun-bath,' flinging up a shower of sand over her back to a distance of about three metres by strong simultaneous jerks of her forelimbs. Her course was zig-zag and she even doubled back upon her tracks searching for a suitable place in which to rest. Meanwhile she was completely coated with sand, except for her eyes, which were washed by a copious flow of tears!"

So the turtle's tears are functional, not emotional, and Alice's Mock Turtle probably only had sand in his eyes when he discoursed to her about "ancient mystery and seaography," two subjects turtles seem deeply versed in. Indeed, ancient mystery is never forgotten, and the machinery that is set in motion when the forementioned nest-digging begins grinds inexorably on to its appointed end come hell and high water. Even a sharp blow on the head may go unnoticed by the egg-laying turtle, and natives often place a gourd or other container beneath the tail of laying females to catch the eggs straight from the factory.

The Loggerheads go through much the same performance, and only one first-hand account of it appears to exist. About an hour before dusk on July 11, 1910, Dr. Mast of Johns Hopkins happened to be within a few yards of where I now stood on Loggerhead Key, when, he reports, a large turtle came out of the sea. It was a Loggerhead and she came directly up the beach for about sixty feet, where she immediately began to make her nest. Using both body movements and flippers she dug a crescent-shaped trench in the sand, wide and deep in the middle, shallow at both ends. The front flippers acted as anchors. When it was finished, the turtle took a position so that the right hind leg was over the middle of the bottom. This flipper was then thrust into the sand and the end turned up like a partly closed hand. It was raised, and the handful of sand thrown out. Then the left flipper repeated the process, and the two alternately scooped the sand from the nest until a deep cylindrical hole had been dug. The turtle then maneuvered so that her back end was over the hole and the egg-laying began. Eggs were dropped one or two at a time every few seconds until there were more than a hundred in the hole. Immediately after the laying was finished, the turtle began to cover the eggs. The fore flippers still served as anchors, while the hind flippers and body swung from side to side, scraping sand beneath her until the trench as well as the hole was filled. Finally she turned about over the region several times, scattering sand in every direction with all four flippers so as to conceal the place. This action does not hide the telltale signs of nest-making, but it does make it difficult to find the exact spot where the eggs are buried. Fishermen confirm this, and Deraniyagala states that the Leatherback he was watching, though appearing not to move from the nest, actually shifted more than six feet away from it during ten minutes of working over the surface.

The whole process of nest-making, egg-laying and nest-hiding is an extremely complex and prolonged action, not of the intelligence but of deep, unconscious instinct, which drives inevitably in sequence from one step to the next until it is all over. Whatever the interruption, the process is picked up where it was left off, and even turning a turtle on its back may not stop the laying of the eggs. Ultimately the tension lessens, and to quote Deraniyagala once more, "at this stage I struck her a sharp blow on the head with a stick and sat upon her, but undeterred she continued to churn up the sand and worked shoreward instead of towards the sea. After a time she doubled back on her tracks and slowly and laboriously repeated the process. Finally she decided that her duty was done, and it was certainly very thorough, for after she had gone, three of us dug for an hour with our hands but were unable to locate the eggs. The departing turtle no longer showered sand with her forelimbs, but wanly made for the sea, stopping every two or three shuffles, blowing most of the time. Gradually she recovered her energy and rested only after every ten or fifteen seconds. She approached the wave line and there paused. The breakers were rough on that night at Tangalla. When the surf reached her, she allowed herself to be washed away into the waves without exerting herself. At her first attempt she failed to get past the breakers, but as the next wave rose she hugged the ground, escaped under the wave, and was gone."

Sea turtles have an ancient lineage. As reptiles, they have been laying their land-based reptilian eggs for more than two hundred million years, and as land turtles with an armor of tortoise-shell, as we know them, they have existed almost as long a time. They took to the sea (those that became sea turtles) quite recently—no more than sixty million years ago. Around the time the first rash of rampaging warm-blooded hairy mammals overran the land, the ancestral turtle went seaward, probably as a refuge. It eventually made the change permanent, and as the centuries and millennia rolled by, slowly transformed the clumsy tortoise leg into the flipper of a swimmer. If you go into any museum today you can see that the bones of the old legs are still there, molded and stretched into a paddle to be sure, but for all that still recognizable in the skeleton, piece by piece with even the bones of your own hand and arm. Look upon it and wonder, for it is this flipper that was once the stumpy leg of a tortoise, and must still be used as a leg in struggling up the sand and digging a nest. For the eggs tie the sea turtle to the land, and the land demands that it walk and dig, however awkwardly.

Sea turtles grow to large size, but even a fairly large turtle goes in fear of its life. William Beebe found a fifty-pound specimen cut from the stomach of a thirteen-foot tiger shark. Yet no enemies can compare with man himself. We take both eggs and adults, the more and bigger the better, particularly those of the Green Turtles. These are supposed to make the best soup, and they are the easiest to catch. Like most vegetarians, with the exception of George Bernard Shaw, the Green Turtles are somewhat sluggish when compared with their omnivorous and carnivorous relatives, and lack the aggressiveness of the Loggerhead and the Hawksbill. The Green Turtle feeds for the most part on turtle grass or eel grass, which are not seaweeds but flowering grasses that have left the land for the sea (as indeed the turtle has). However, the salad is garnished with small mollusks, crustaceans and even the shell-less flying snails of the surface waters. Other turtles concentrate on a meat diet without much apparent discrimination, and even the Loggerhead sponge is eaten, though possibly for the myriad of crustaceans and worms that live inside it rather than for any taste for sponge as sponge. Sponges, for all their purity in the bathtub, have probably the most offensive odors of any living animal, skunk included. Of course, when swallowed with a copious draft of salt water by a hungry turtle with nostrils closed, the smell may not be noticeable.

I suppose since they do eat sponges, there is no reason to feel surprised that turtles also seem to enjoy jellyfishes. All kinds of turtles devour them. Giant Leatherbacks have been found with their stomachs full of them, while Hawksbills even eat that notorious stinger of the seas, the Portuguese man-of-war, though they have sense enough to keep their eyes closed during the process. Turtle-hunters have known this for a long time and take advantage of the turtle's shut-eyed preoccupation. Whether jellyfish or man-of-war, it takes a lot to make a little of these animals, which are more than 95 per cent water, and perhaps the explanation of their place on the turtle's menu is that in his case it takes a little to keep a lot going—according to one physiologist six ounces of banana takes care of the energy needs of a nine-pound turtle for one month.

Leatherbacks may attain a weight of close to 1,500 pounds. Large size generally suggests a long life, a half truth when you consider that an eighty-ton whale probably dies of old age when it is about twenty years old. The giant land tortoises are thought to be Methuselahs that grow a little faster than a stone, and the larger sea turtles to be even older. This is only partly true. Turtles of both sea and land do reach a really ripe old age, and one individual on the island of Mauritius is known for certain to have been at least 152, and perhaps 200, years old when accidental death overtook it. What is really surprising is the rapidity of the turtle's growth. Green Turtles, which are typical, grow to a length of eight inches during their first year and add about one-half pound and half an inch to their shell each month. Four-year-old Loggerheads can weigh eighty pounds and a mature 200-pounder may be no older than ten years.

For all their dependence on the oceans, sea turtles are as truly air-breathing as any land tortoise or lizard. Sooner or later they must come to the surface to breathe. On the other hand, they are able to dive and remain below for an hour or more. But like all four-footed vertebrate animals they need to rest and sleep at times. Not so long ago it was safe enough to come ashore and bask or drowse in the sun on the ledges and sand bars of lonely islands and empty shores. Now that there are practically no empty shores and they have learned better, a snoozing turtle is generally seen only out at sea. In fact, some Rhode Island fishermen convinced the late Victorian naturalist Bumpus that turtles go to sleep with their heads resting on lobster buoys, but this, I feel, merely indicates that fishermen have lively imaginations and a biologist, for all his scientific method, can be as credulous as any other variety of the human species.

Turtle hunting goes back a long way, for both turtles and human civilizations have found the Mediterranean, for one place, much to their liking, though the turtles have had quite a struggle to survive long enough to prove it. The most ingenious method of catching turtles belongs however to the islands of the western oceans, the Atlantic and Pacific. The first report of the method comes from Columbus, in his account of the second voyage, two summers after his first discovery of the Indies. He was sailing among the islets off the south coast of Cuba when, "on the following day, when the Admiral was very anxious to have speech, there came a canoe to hunt fish. And so they call it hunting, because they hunt some fish with others. For they have certain fish, fastened at the tail with cords, and these fish are the shape of congers and have a large mouth, all full of suckers like the cuttle-fish, and they are very daring, as ferrets are here. And when they are thrown into the water, they go to fasten themselves on some fish; of these they do not leave hold in the water but only when they are pulled out. . . . They had one of these fish fastened on the bottom on a large turtle, and they waited to get it into the canoe, which they did."

The fish has since been fully identified as the Remora, or shark sucker. It is not an eel and it does not have suckers in its mouth, but the dorsal fin is modified to form a complicated sucker on top of the head. The Remora attaches itself by

means of its sucker to any passing turtle or shark, or any other
large fish, merely to get a free ride and in the hope of sharing
a meal at the end of the journey. Probably they hitch on to
ship bottoms more than we know: its older name is the Ship-
holder, and its Latin name, Echineis, means "holding back."
Pictures of the Remora appear on Greek and Roman vases,
and Pliny wrote that the death of the Emperor Caligula was
due to his great galley being held up by a Remora while the
rest of the fleet made its escape.

But perhaps the most adventurous turtle of them all is
Theodore, now residing in the aquarium of the London Zoo.
Theodore is a Mexican Loggerhead that turned up flippering
placidly along a seashore highway on the Cornish coast, sending Cornishmen into a dither of excitement, for they knew his
home lay several thousand miles away in the Gulf of Mexico,
possibly in these very Dry Tortugas. He may have been a
sleepy youngster who woke up too late, or one who paddled
too soon too far from shore and got caught up in the Gulf
Stream racing past his front door in the Keys. In a couple of
years at most, traveling one mile an hour, or 8,760 miles a
year, and allowing for delays, the Stream would bring him
close to European shores. What, after all, is time to a turtle,
who cares little where he goes, or when he gets there? At that,
the water must have been getting a bit chilly by the time
Theodore made his landfall, and his preference for the high-
ways of Cornwall indicated he'd had a bellyful of sea-riding
for a long time.

CHAPTER THREE

THE BIRTH AND DEATH OF AN ISLAND

SEA BIRDS are fishermen, and where the fish go the birds are sure to follow, particularly if they have the added attraction of a lagoon lying between keys and reefs, where eggs can be laid without fear of rats or men, and fish caught abundantly to feed the young.

Our keys were no exception, and Bush Key, three miles across the lagoon, was an island of birds. Most of them were there to breed, though some, like the frigates, visit the lagoon just for the summer fishing, and breed far away. Large, soaring creatures that lightly carried their full title, the Magnificent Man-o'-War Bird, the frigates rested on the bare branches of dead mangroves or sailed high overhead, dark and powerful, with the great, hooked beaks of birds of prey, sailors before the wind second only to the wandering albatross, and with relative wingspread and flight muscles matched by none. Elsewhere on Bush Key the terns took over. Sooty terns nested everywhere, if you can use the word "nest" for the laying of one or two mottled eggs on a patch of flat sand. They crowded so closely that you had to watch your step or risk crushing an egg or a fledgling. Even a brooding mother moved only at the last moment, and then in protesting reluctance, while the males, less occupied by their paternity and tired of fishing, collected in windrows on the open beach. The noddy terns, a little fussier than their companions and scorning the bare sand, make a nest a little more worthy of the name, either among the lower branches of the mangroves or in the green, fleshy Sesuvium scrub covering much of the island.

Keys and terns—islands and birds—are closely related and have had a curious history. When the Laboratory on Loggerhead Key first started at the turn of the century, nearby Bush Key was no more than a barren sand bar awash with the tide, while colonies of sooty and noddy terns nested on Bird Key, an extensive island at that time but now in its turn little more than a sandy shoal. Between them, Bird Key and Bush Key, they show the island cycle, from birth through life to death and new birth.

Bush Key now and Bird Key in its time have been held immune from the scouring of the currents and the blast of the hurricane because of their green cover of vegetation, a cover which the nesting birds deem necessary for their breeding. But birds excrete guano, semi-solid and so rich in phosphates that industries have been based upon it. Yet that which enriches the soil as the most valuable of all fertilizers will burn the living plant if it should actually touch it. So the thousands of terns, perching and nesting among the mangrove and scrub, scorch and kill the leaves and branches which bear them, by day and by night, year after year, until slowly the green world dies from the island. The dead bushes remain for awhile but not very long. The roots rot, the swirling waters etch farther and farther back into the sand that holds them, and soon the scrub has blown away and the sands washed into the current. Through its green hospitality the island has committed suicide, and no more remains than a shallow bank of sand resting on old reefs and covered by the tide.

This has happened to Bird Key in recent years, although now that the slate has been wiped clean a fresh start is being made, a sand bar is beginning once again to rise above highwater, and there may, by the process described in a moment, be another new Bird Key in a few years. The terns were lucky to have Bush Key as an alternative when the crisis approached. Bush Key, at first home to just a few birds, has grown enormously (and its bird-population with it) since the beginning of this century. At that time there was only a little sand above the wash of the waves. Now you can walk over nineteen acres, and near the center, surrounded by groves of white mangroves, feet squash the mire of brackish and freshwater pools. You can forget entirely that blue, deep ocean encircles you no farther away than a crab can scuttle. But bare areas are increasing as the birds nest and perch by the thousands. It may even be the beginning of the end of the vegetation and of the island itself. Perhaps Bird Key will be ready to take over again when the time comes to move.

Reefs will eventually bring the sand to the surface, but it takes more than reefs and sand to make an island, and the world above the waves must play its part. There are plants that can grow in sand, but even for them the sand must be more or less stable, and for this the elements somehow manage to pave the way. Walking along the beach on Loggerhead Key one evening, just above the wash of the tide, I slipped, taking my weight on two or three fingertips. It felt as though these fingers were shattered, and what I had taken for rather

dense, damp sand, turned out to be a two-inch crust of sandstone overlying soft sand. It could be cracked only by jumping
on it. Rain running into and off the sloping beach had leached
away some of the salts and changed the mixture until it set
as a kind of cement, binding the particles of sand together,
and to an extent it had sealed off the edge of the island against
the waves.

Yet it takes more than reefs and sand—even with a sandstone crust for protection—to make an island, and plants must
pioneer the way. Above all others, the seeds of the red mangrove should be called the island-makers. An island that is not
actually rock needs to be bound over by a green cover if it is
to live. Think what the colonists must be. They must be able,
first, to reach the sand bars and the reefs. They must be able,
second, to anchor themselves and live with their roots in salt
water. And they must, third, create conditions that help build
up the land and make it congenial to other plants.

The red mangrove has everything the maritime colonist
needs. Young plants anchor themselves and grow rapidly in
shallow water between sheltering sand bars, rooting, in the
sea itself, into the marine soil of sand and shell fragments.
Tiers of prop-roots, or buttresses, spring out and down, so that
each young seedling appears to be clutching at the ground
beneath the sea with a many-fingered hand. More and better
soils rapidly accumulate among the tangled submarine stems,
and other green invaders of the sea grow thickly around, the
turtle and manatee grasses.

Columbus thought of the mangroves when he was caught in
a storm at the end of his first voyage almost within sight of the
Azores. At a time when he felt all would be lost, and so fearful

that his discoveries would remain unknown that he wrote an account of them on parchment and cast it overboard in a barrel, the mangrove came to his mind as a symbol of peace and soft breezes. He thought, mistakenly, that there could simply be no storms where gentle trees rooted in the edge of the sea itself. He did not know that after the hurricanes pass and palm-trees and buildings lie shattered, the buttressed mangroves stand as they did before.

How do they reach the sandy shoals in the first place? Neither wind nor birds can carry their seeds, for they develop on the branches of the parent trees and grow into long, heavy seedlings before dropping off. When they do, they are usually six to eight inches long, stout embodiments of a race that floats and flourishes in salt water. They may drop straight down into mud at the base of the parent mangrove, or be carried a few feet away before lodging, to grow and branch and in time transform a solitary tree into a mangrove forest. Or they may drop into the swirling water of high tide and be swept from the parent thicket far out to sea.

It appears that the mangroves of the tropical Americas actually crossed the Atlantic ocean itself, from Africa, as seedlings drifting for weeks with the equatorial currents. Perhaps no man knows more about them than one of my Loggerhead Key colleagues, John Davis, a Professor of Botany at the University of Florida and a plant geographer who has made mangroves, as well as the Everglades, a specialty. Davis, who has worked the Tortugas, Marquesas and mainland groves, in the face of a living mosquito hell, had collected thousands of mature seedlings, painted them separately with different colors, and cast them overboard at various places. Some that were launched between Key West and the Tortugas landed on the broad strand of Loggerhead Key. Many others arrived at the same beach besides those that had been marked, and Davis reckoned that at least 10,000, and probably a much greater number, were launched from the mainland each year to drift in the direction of the Tortugas.

CHAPTER FOUR

THE REEF AND THE WORM

THE tide was low and a line of reef lay dry above the blue and green sea that imprisoned our island. Boulders lay scattered in the shoal water along the edge of the lagoon, their coral heads thrust into the air. You could wade out for a hundred yards before you had to swim or go back. But cross the reef to its outer side, where the water chopped and chirped before the breeze, and you were over your head with one step, for the slope was steep. It is always so on the "live," growing side of a reef, and here the colors deepened quickly from the light shades of the glaring shallow into the darker green and blue of deep water.

Coral reefs are alive, even though most of their actual substance may be merely the dead product of past life. And while there are many questions about reefs that are not fully answered, we come in the last analysis to the basic answer that the sea is very salt, that many animals and plants have found it both possible and profitable to precipitate out the less-soluble of these salts to form their own limy shells or skeletons, which long survive, as reefs, the death of the organisms that produced them.

Reefs are no place for bare feet. Coral, dead or alive, can cut them to ribbons; seemingly harmless little sponges can slip fine needles of lime or silica into your skin; sea urchins, those porcupine-like relatives of the starfish whose round, brittle shells you can smash against a rock like the gulls do, boast a spine that may puncture your skin, to break off and fester within. And unless you step carefully among the rocks and dazzling water, an inch or so of the poison-tipped, foot-long, needle-pointed spines of the black urchin of the coral seas, the Diadem, may pierce your flesh with the throbbing pain of ten bee stings rolled into one. Its sting is not danger-ous, except to your morale. Not so the ugly and almost invis-ible Stonefish that inhabits the 1,200-mile-long Great Barrier Reef of Australia and refuses to move from your path. It merely erects thirteen poisoned spines for you to walk on, causing days of agony and possibly death.

Though this spiny-skinned group, including the urchins, starfishes and sea lilies, is literally as old as the hills, with its skeletons abounding in the oldest of all fossil-bearing rocks (the four to five hundred million-year-old Cambrian and Si-lurian) yet you can find them living about the reef today in diverse modern costume. Turn over a large boulder and look quickly at the shallow, agitated pool beneath—black, five-armed brittle stars slide in frantic and sinuous haste for the shade, and maybe a reef Synapta looking like a two-foot sand-colored worm as thick as your finger will squirm to get out of the sun. It's not a worm at all, but another member of the Sign of Five, and if you look into its mouth you'll find that like the starfish and urchin everything radiates from the center in fives and twice-fives, although it can wriggle worm-like into dark, narrow places to feed and reproduce in safety.

Walk to the outer side of the reef and you'll find an urchin whose spines are short and not poisonous, and whose body is no longer round but egg-shaped. Try to pick it up and you'll find you need a crowbar, for it has worked its way into the soft coral sandstone when it was small, and as it grew etched and ground the hole around and beneath it until at last it was a prisoner of its own industry. Is it safe, has it dug its own grave or was it simply trapped like Alice was within the house of the White Rabbit?

You may, among the weed-covered boulders at the edge of the warm sea, find the sea hare, no rabbit, but a large, seemingly shell-less snail with a pair of long, pointed ears which are really tentacles. It has a few tricks of its own, with its yellow, brown and green markings that make it difficult for any but a quick eye to spot. If you poke it, it sheds a rich, purple cloud, confusing enough to sight and devastating to any sense of smell a fish may have. And you cannot call it he or she, for like most snails it is both together and can only be called "it."

In a little deeper water, motionless but for the swaying it shares with the weed fronds, the basket stars rest delicately on numberless fingertips. The tips curl up like the snaky locks of Medusa when the star is disturbed, and its scientific name is indeed Gorgonocephalus, for the head of that mythological monster whose gaze turned men to stone.

But isolated individuals, for all their ingenious natures, do not give rise to reefs, though their pulverized remains may be swept together by the waves and tossed up to make part of a shell or coral beach. Reefs are formed only when certain conditions are met. The reef-producing organisms must live in closely-packed communities, and their supporting skeletons and protective shells must remain in place after death. Only then can new life keep growing on the surface of the old, and gradually massive calcareous structures can be built up to form the reef.

These reef-builders are of several kinds—corals of various sorts, certain marine worms, and some primitive stony seaweeds called nullipores. All three play their part in building a rampart against the sea. But the reef itself is almost entirely limestone, a single substance reflecting not at all the diversity of the animals and plants that built it, but the constant, though complex, chemical composition of the sea itself.

The coral animal can exist in reef-producing compactness only so long as food, oxygen and light can reach it. Since there is not enough of these three in the dark depths, coral does not grow except where the currents sweep and sunlight penetrates. Each little coral cup, like a small, stony sea anemone enveloped in a transparent veil of life, reaches into the swirling waters for sustenance. New cups grow from the side of older cups, and great coral creations rise, large branching staghorns, compact boulders of brain coral, all likely to be surmounted by the soft corals, the beautiful sea fans and sea rods, among whose branches the exotically brilliant coral fish dart and hover like the butterflies and birds of the flowering earth.

The coral's secret, or part of it, lies in an ancient partnership. Animal coral tissue is filled with a multitude of microscopic living plants, and the metabolism of the two, plant and animal, so interlock that as long as the outside energy of light is available to the plant, it absorbs the chemical wastes of the animal tissues. Without them, corals would merely smother in the congested masses that make a reef, perishing for lack of space in which to find their food and oxygen. As it is, even with plant help, a reef remains healthy only along its outer side; its inner slope is cluttered with the dead and dying.

On the rough seaward edge the corals maintain their own kingdom, forever growing out against the force of the waves that bring them a better food supply and wash away clogging debris. If the reef breaks, letting strong currents flow along both inner and outer walls, the reef animals grow on both sides, and the crest along the middle ages and dies and is hollowed away by the driving sea. The living reef that remains may then rise sixty feet from its platform on the sea floor like a row of giant hollow teeth awash in the ocean, with cavities twenty feet across and just as deep. These are the "boilers," and they make the finest natural aquaria in the world. But if you find them, be careful, for the swell of the outer sea swirling over the rim may sweep you into the depths, too stunned to be anything but food for fishes.

Reefs are never all coral. The stony algae, the corals of the plant world, contribute massively to the reef foundations at depths they alone can enjoy. Then some newcomers go into action, the mason worms, which add a tough, resistant coat to the outer surfaces of the walls, and buttress the reef with the countless hard tubes they make as homes. Even then the reef is not complete—every crevice is a haven for some sort of sea beast, often with a bizarre beauty of its own.

Go to the edge of a reef after sundown, or anchor a boat over it if the tide is high, hold a light just above the water, and wait and watch. If the time is right, sea worms will come swarming to the surface, rising from among the corals and rocks to the light because they are ready to spawn.

Long Key, in the Dry Tortugas, shelters another worm that hides in the reef and takes no part in its building. It is the Atlantic Palolo, and its name belongs not to the Atlantic at all but to the Pacific. There, among the islands of Samoa, on a definite date every year, a week after the full moon in November, *rear* halves of countless millions of worms back out of their burrows and break off. They swim upward to shed eggs and sperm, starting the next generation, while the old front stump creeps quietly back into its corner down below to grow a new tail and repeat the process the following year. Such numbers appear on the surface that the sea has been compared with vermicelli soup, and indeed the Samoans take the worms as a great delicacy. About two days before the spawning the water becomes cloudy. Then, just before dawn on the appointed day the swarming begins. Two or three hours later it is all over and they are gone, but in the meantime the local populace gather them in handnets and baskets, rapidly filling their canoes. At the Palolo feast that follows, the worms are wrapped in bread-fruit leaves and cooked in ground-ovens, though the more enthusiastic eat them raw.

The Palolo is now known not only in the Pacific islands but also from the coast of Japan and the Caribbean. The name Palolo is not given to a particular worm, but to any marine worm behaving in this characteristic way. The Palolo of Samoa is undoubtedly the most famous, for gastronomical reasons, but it has been left for the Atlantic Palolo to excite a more intellectual interest, for the spawning of our own

Palolo occurs in July rather than November, and even allowing for the fact that Samoa and the Tortugas lie on opposite sides of the equator, where seasons differ, the times are still out of phase.

Since 1898 the spawning times of the Palolo have been recorded in the Tortugas, for the forty years that biologists have visited the keys. Many have studied the worms, going as far as Samoa to make comparisons. Now you would think that so much effort directed at a wriggling worm would leave little unsolved, and the question which comes to mind, a basic one, is—why bother? There are many answers, but I feel the real one is the answer that perhaps only the artist would understand. The true artist *must,* under compulsion, express in some medium what he sees and feels. The scientist is much the same, however remote his circumstances must make him appear. There is no other valid explanation, and it is not enough to say, "I study certain low forms of life because they are interesting." It would be more truthful to say, "I study them because I am fascinated and cannot help myself," or perhaps, "I am vitally concerned—for my own sake and while I can live and savor what I know—in finding out what I am doing on this planet!"

So it is that men have wondered about the spawning of Palolo as Galileo wondered about the movement of the earth and stars, and when they have been biologists their curiosity has not been easily satisfied.

When Alfred Goldsborough Mayer became the first director of the Laboratory at Loggerhead he had time to watch the Palolos, and described them vividly. (It was he, incidentally, who went on behalf of Palolo to Samoa.) Before sunrise on the morning of the first swarming day, he noted, the worm crawls out backwards from its reef-bound burrow until all the sexual segments and a portion of the slender middle part of its body protrude. A vigorous helical, corkscrew-like twisting movement then comes over the sexual segments. They are twisted off, and on being set free swim vertically to the surface where they swim rapidly along, still backward. The male ends are salmon-red or dull pink, the females greenish gray from the color of the egg mass within.

When the first, faint rays of sunrise light fall upon the ocean, the worms contract violently, the skin tears and eggs and sperm are shed into the water. Meanwhile, the front halves of the worms far below creep back into their burrows, and the regeneration of new hind-ends begins. Immature worms play no part in the process.

The swarming of the sexual ends of mature worms generally occurs a few days after the full moon in July, and although the time may vary slightly in different localities, it appears between 353 and 369 days after that of the year before. The long cycle of the year begins with the swarming itself and these front ends that creep back into the holes in the coral reef. If you dig out a few two or three weeks later, you find a new tail has already been made, in miniature, but with all the lost segments already present. The tail grows slowly until, early in the following year, innumerable forerunners of eggs or sperm begin to show. These grow and gain their own maturity by June or July, when they are ready for the swarm. The long process is regulated by the temperature of the sea and final ripening is no more nor less mysterious than the annual flowering of spring bulbs and summer lilies at their appointed time.

It is this precise timing that is almost uncanny. How do the controls operate? Why should the behavior of a worm on the sea floor synchronize with such cosmic cycles as the earth's revolution about the sun and the moon's about the earth? Why should the swarming occur during the night of the first or third quarter of the July moon?

When sea animals react according to the phase of the moon, there is always a suspicion that the connection is indirect—that the moon simply determines the time of high and low tides and it is the tides that really influence the animals. Not so in the case of Palolo, where tidal effects were shown long ago to be unimportant. No, it was light, and the absence of light, that were playing dominant roles in the life of the worm. And midsummer moonlight, it was found, had the opposite effect on Palolo from that on a man and a maid.

According to the meteorological tables of the Smithsonian Institution, moonlight reaches a maximum intensity of 0.02 foot-candles at the full moon and is only one-tenth as bright at the quarter. At the Carnegie Lab on Loggerhead Key while I was there two investigators, Leonard Clark and Walter Hess (both of them college biology professors) ascertained that immature worms retreat into the darkness of their burrow when light intensity exceeds 0.01 foot-candles, but move out toward the light when it gets weaker than that. Thus they remain out of sight during the day and emerge to feed only during the night, and not then if the moon is full. The sexual ends of mature worms, on the other end, are strongly attracted to light of almost any intensity.

So we can analyze the July swarming a little better. Before July the worms are not mature and their eggs are not able to develop. After they become fully ripe, two opportunities for swarming occur. Those worms that are ready to spawn by the first quarter of the moon are called forth by the moonlight of the quarter-moon intensity. A fair-sized swarm does usually appear at the surface at that time. But as the moon waxes to the full and beyond, the intensity of the light exceeds the critical 0.01 foot-candle and the worms are held in their burrow, and while they wait more and more of them become mature and ready to burst. And then, as soon as the moonlight becomes weak enough to attract and not repel them, and as soon as the sun has gone down, the major event begins, and each night for several nights every Palolo that is ready backs out of its burrow and allows its hind-end to twist off and soar to the surface.

Even broken pieces of back ends spiral their way toward the light of the moon, and it is suggestive that pieces of worm devoid of nerve centers, eyes or any other sense organs (though they have a nerve cord through the whole body length) should be so sensitive and responsive to light. Even the eyeless earthworms that we dig for bait can tell whether they are going toward light or dark, and it may be that all life is itself at least in part a creation of the light that blazes through the universe, and that all living substance is in some degree conscious of light, whether it has eyes or not.

CHAPTER FIVE

THE MOAT

THE great red walls of the fort cut sharply against the sky. There were no clouds, yet the light pouring into the enclosure was white in its intensity. The sun stabbed with strong, brilliant rays, intent on blasting all shade from the earth.

Midsummer noon on the edge of the Tropic of Cancer was like the Equator itself. The sun blazed from its zenith, and the shadow of the date palm was a little pool shriveled close to the base of the trunk. Yet there was still a shimmer of green from the short grass carpeting the old parade ground. And in the silence I reached for a cluster of small, purplish dates from this long-forgotten tree and found them sweet.

There was no breeze, no sound, no movement of any kind as I walked toward the darkness within the walls, and only the echo of my own thoughts came out to meet me. But on those echoes came the ghosts of the fort, of the men who had died hopelessly in what had once been the Devil's Island of America.

The fort was Fort Jefferson, a century old, with little in its still beauty to suggest either the drama of its past or the startling present-day outlook from its ramparts. From the top of any of its six high walls the horizon is the far, flat edge of the sea, blurred only by the squalls forever vexing the waters of the Gulf. The low coasts of the Everglades and Cuba lie out of sight beyond the curve of the ocean, and only the little sand keys that made up the rest of the Tortugas Atoll are visible as if clustering around the fort for protection. The fort is built to guard the harbor that lies between the keys and appears to stand fully bastioned from the sea itself, like the last high tower of the lost Atlantis sinking beneath the waves.

A Union garrison held the Fort during the Civil War, and during the aftermath it held a thousand prisoners, rockbound by the walls, cut off from the mainland by a hundred miles of dangerous waters, and, as if that were not enough, encircled by the Moat. In those days the Moat was kept alive with sharks, and only madness would lead a man to try to scale the walls, defy the sharks and swim the Gulf of Mexico. Yet madness there must have been, for shortly after the war the prison was swept by yellow fever and even the physician died. The only medical help left was a prisoner himself, one Dr. Mudd, who had unwittingly given medical help to Lincoln's assassin. He too was stricken and his health broken, and though later freed, he died in poverty. "If he catches me, my name is mud," is an expression said to have originated with the unhappy doctor's case.

Fort, then prison, Jefferson was abandoned for forty years, only to serve in 1898 as a coaling station during the Spanish-American War. Now at last a sinister and evil work of man has become a refuge for beauty, and the spirit of beauty reigns both within and without its walls. Its ancient misery is now muted by the winds, the Moat holds the jellyfish medusa but not the shark, and sea birds nest unmolested where they will.

The channel marker leaned to the current and a brown

pelican flew listlessly away as I came around the edge of the
dock that morning, while all around sooty terns sat on their
eggs or young wherever there was space and a little shelter
from the wind.

The old dock was ramshackle but it did offer shade on the
sand below and escape not so much from the heat, which was
comfortable, as from the intolerable light. It was a relief to
wade in the shallow water beneath the ramp, until company
arrived. A small barracuda kept pace with me about ten feet
offshore, slipping ahead when I moved, stopping when I stood
still. Not more than two feet long, it looked harmless enough,
but a split-second dash inshore and a slash across an ankle
could be dangerous for anyone alone on an island, and imagination took hold as my naked feet sought the dry land. Anyway, my business lay with the jellyfish in the Moat.

On this side of the fort the sand had drifted to a wide
bank, level with the top of the Moat's outer wall, where some
had slipped over. Within the Moat the water was only a few
feet deep and almost stagnant. Yet jellyfish were there in
abundance, perhaps in their own zoological circle almost as
well-known as the fort itself. They are medusae named after
Cassiopeia, with ethereal color, rhythmic grace and perfect
symmetry. The Cassiopeia medusa, unlike the rest of its kind,
spends most of its life on its back, and those in the Moat below
were no exception. A young naturalist, Robert Payne Bigelow,
first found this particular kind late in the last century near
Port Henderson, Jamaica.

"The bay is overhung by low cashew and mangrove trees,"
he wrote, describing the setting. "At one side is a sunny spot
where a crocodile has made its bed, and a fresh zigzag mark

showed where it had recently slid into the water. A school of fish was circling about in the clear water, and barnacles and sea anemones spread their tentacles from the submerged roots of the mangroves, while the bottom at the inner end of the bay was completely carpeted by a colony of beautiful rhizo-stomatous medusae. A few very small specimens might be seen swimming about, but most of the medusae, especially the larger ones, would not ordinarily leave the bottom. They lay upon their backs, with their voluminous, branching mouth parts spread out over their discs, which were motionless, except for occasional flaps of their margins. If any of these animals were disturbed, they would, however, swim about like ordinary medusae; but before long they would settle down again and assume their usual attitude upon the bottom. Within this limited area there were countless numbers of them, and in many places they were so thickly spread that their margins touched upon all sides, or even overlapped. The spectacle . . . was truly marvelous."

This is an unusual habit for jellyfish, but certainly a good one under the circumstances. It has two possible explanations. Food is abundant and far more concentrated in the shallow bays and lagoons than in the open ocean, and it may well be that in these shallows the only security a jellyfish can attain is by lying still on the bottom (upside down in order to eat) where the coming and going of the tide could not strand it. Or perhaps, since our Cassiopeia is a comparatively substantial lady, possibly no more than nine-tenths water instead of the customary nineteen-twentieths, it may be just too much effort to keep moving all the time. So she rests on her broad back, with mouth and tentacles fishing avidly upwards.

Some of her color is not her own. Like corals, some sea anemones, and the giant man-trapping clams of the South Pacific, her tissues are alive with microscopic greenish plant-cells, green with chlorophyll that produces starch and cellulose and oxygen. This makes the medusa a little less dependent on the oxygen in the water and it can survive successfully in the semi-stagnant mangrove pools and ancient moats.

Not that jellyfish are designed for moats and mud-flats. Huge, pulsating discs, sometimes seven feet across with a hundred-or-more feet of tentacles streaming behind, they belong to the wide ocean, have come into being with the ocean, and in great measure partake of the very ocean itself. They go where the sweep of the currents takes them, but with one waiting danger—there is disaster and death, not overhead nor anywhere around them, but waiting forever below—not a living menace but the lethal pull of the earth itself, away from the light of the sun.

Life lives in the light, and when medusae sink into the dark night below, they starve and die. What needs they have are simple but they must be met. Being animals they must eat, and so they have tentacles, a mouth and a stomach. Being a little heavier than water they tend to sink, and so have nerve and muscle. And since they must swim away from the earth toward the sun, lest they lose themselves in perpetual darkness, they can sense both gravity and light. There can be no rest, no sleep, no more than a heart can find between two beats.

There is little in the world, however, that can eat, swim and sense the earth and sun much more simply than a jellyfish. Because of this—or perhaps because we have intuitively recognized its primeval antiquity—scientists, a very few to be sure, have sailed the seas and searched out the island lagoons, determined that the ancient Cassiopeia yield up her mystery and that of the ocean that cradles her. The greatest of these was Alfred Goldsborough Mayer, who inspired by Alexander and Louis Agassiz, famous zoologists of the past century, toured the world from 1890 to the early 1900s. His offering to his Goddess and to science is his *Medusa of the World,* "replete," he says, "with memories of the ocean in many moods, of the palm-edged lagoons of coral islands sparkling in the tropic sun, of the cold gray waters of the northern sea bestrewn with floating ice, of days of withering calm in the heat of the torrid zone, and of adventure in the hurricane."

What makes a jellyfish?

It is almost entirely water, yet it has pattern, beauty of form and color, action, responsiveness. It is, in short, alive. The water within it and around it is salt, so salty that a man will die uncomfortably if he drinks much of it. And yet this salt is the salt of its life. If you place a jellyfish in fresh water it will die quickly, and so will most animals that live in the sea. Mayer discovered something of the meaning of this when he first began his work at Loggerhead Key, a bare three miles from the Fort where he, like myself years later, found Cassiopeia conveniently at hand, resting in the Moat.

Sea water is what physiologists call a "balanced fluid," like your blood. Both are salt, and in both the salts are of sodium, potassium and calcium, carefully balanced against each other. This particular balance goes to the very root of all living matter, as Cassiopeia in the hands of Mayer has shown. The

large, pulsating bell that swims through the water does so by
means of its sheath of muscle and network of nerves. In normal sea water, as long as the salt concentrations are balanced,
the nerve impulses are neatly controlled by the sense organs
along the margin of the bell. But Mayer found that if there
was an excess of sodium salts, nerve and muscle became grossly
stimulated, and Cassiopeia was incapacitated by the violence
of the contractions. If there was too much of the other salts,
all sensitivity was lost and no contractions took place at all.
Life was normal only as long as salt balance was normal. The
salt of the sea penetrates to the very core of jellyfish existence.

Yet if normal, balanced sea water is so soothing, what makes
a jelly-fish swim? Mayer found the answer to this too. Each
tiny gravity sense-club hanging from the margin of the medusa
sets free a chemical which brings about a local excess of sodium, and this in turn stimulates the nerve net. If the clubs
are removed the animal is paralyzed. In action, first one club
and then another sets off a contraction of the swimming bell,
and the medusa is kept in motion, afloat and alive. Light that
strikes the simple eye-spots along the edge acts in much the
same way, and between gravity club and light-sensitive eye
the jellyfish is kept away from the darkness below and forever
striving toward the surface of the sea.

The pulse of a medusa is the beat of your heart. If you live
near the sea and can keep a few of these hardy jellyfish alive
in a tub, you can repeat one or two now famous experiments.
It is not difficult to graft a pair of Cassiopeias together by a
narrow bridge of tissue, so they become as Siamese twins.
Then whichever of the two medusa beats the faster sets the
pace of the beat for both of them. If the faster one is pinched

to slow it down, the one that was at first the slower now takes over as pacemaker. The heart is much the same, for the slow, automatic beat of the heart muscle is governed by the nervous pacemaker at the top. Like the throb of your heart, the pulse of the bell is an alternating work-and-rest, work-and-rest, until final fatigue calls a halt and you and the jellyfish no longer exist.

Jellyfish feel no pain, for there is no brain or nerve center to record it, and the animal can be cut with no more qualm than in the plucking of a flower. If the outer rim is sheared away, and a large disc is also cut out of the middle, you have left a wide girdle of tissue. Left alone it remains inactive, but if you press at any one place, a wave of muscular contraction sweeps both ways round the circle. Halfway round, the two waves meet head on and cancel each other out. This is what happens when a stimulus is sent in from a sense-club or an eye-spot. But if you press down on one side of the girdle after the double wave has started, the wave on that side is weakened and when the two meet, the stronger wave of the outer side no longer fades out but surges through the crisis and keeps going. And it goes on, 'round and 'round the circle in a rippling wave of almost perpetual motion. Yet it is still a wave of contraction, and there is time for muscle to rest between the passing of the wave and the time of its returning, just as the heart rests for the fraction of a second between beats. And neither medusa strip nor human heart can be made to work during its rest period.

This is not quite the end of the story. The rippling circular strip of jellyfish stays alive for a long time, for, having no rigid skeleton to stick out, it can starve in comfort and merely become smaller and smaller in an orderly manner. While it lives it does something that is mysterious and a little uncanny, something only living matter can do and that not always. New tissue grows slowly inward to close the hole in the center, and from the outer rim new tissue grows outward until all that was cut away is restored, not merely in bulk but in quality, down to the last eye-spot and sense-club. Cassiopeia is smaller but she is back.

Jellyfish damage easily, though all those I saw in the Moat below seemed perfect. This could mean that they had really discovered a sanctuary or simply that they had recovered from their wounds.

My time was passing, and while the adult medusae were obvious enough, the youngest stages that I was here to find might be very difficult to detect. They do not even look like jellyfish and would not be seen more than two or three feet away. Fertilized eggs of Cassiopeia develop into minute oval larvae that glide through the water until they find some small dark corner where they can settle down in safe seclusion. The vast majority are unsuccessful in this and die. But those that do manage to live through their first adventure grow a slender stalk to anchor themselves and acquire a mouth and tentacles like a minute sea anemone.

The only way for me to find these stages was to get down into the lukewarm water. And it was best to do it fully clothed and avoid certain sunburn. It would take only a few minutes to dry off afterward. In about an hour of searching I found some, and with even my pocket lens I could see what was happening. The heads of the larger individuals, only a small fraction of an inch across, were flattening to a disc and becoming remarkably medusa-like. Two or three broke off from their stalks and started to swim away, stardust medusae in a universe of water—in a little while each stalk would grow a new head and eventually send it to voyage forth on its own. But to make doubly sure, while the heads were yet transforming, tiny, almost invisible buds grew out near the top of the stalk, minute pear-shaped bodies that broke away to settle close by and become new polyps. No wonder Cassiopeia is abundant wherever she can be found at all.

It was time to climb dripping from the Moat with a jar of water and polyps intact as the boat returned to pick me up. I left Fort Jefferson to the birds and the pulsating, ever-silent medusa.

CHAPTER SIX

THE POWER AND THE GLORY

THE dock on the west beach of Loggerhead stands in a few feet of crystal clear water, partly sheltered by the curving spit of sand at the north end of the Key. It was early and the morning was still cool. There was plenty of time to watch the life below, before the boat left for the reefs on the far side of the lagoon, our day's destination.

The dock seemed to offer all the shade and shelter of a coral reef, together with the unusual perquisites associated with the back-door of a kitchen. Morning, noon and night the cook walked to the end and dumped a bucket or pan of scraps into the sea. Two or three dozen gray snappers usually hung around, playing or resting in the shadows, and when the cook raised his hands to throw, there was a rush, the snappers and scraps hitting the surface at the same time. Yet if anyone but the cook went out, it was altogether different. As I walked along all the snappers that were close by made a slight but simultaneous turn to one side so as to keep a wary eye. Just to see, I picked up the "grains," or forked harpoons, lying at the head of the pier and held them high. In a flash the fish shot away for deep water, though not for long.

Looking more carefully at the water beyond the dock you could see swarms, possibly millions, of small fish no more than an inch long, all with a blue spot on the head. They hovered over the snappers, which seemed to be feeding upon them. Yet there was something strange about it. The swarm left a clear space around each snapper, about equal to its length. Every time a snapper moved the swarm broke up, but immediately reformed. The swarm kept the same shape and size though the little fish were in motion all the time. They danced together like a swarm of gnats in the summer dusk. But what attracted the swarm to the snapper when there was no reward but death, and what kept them at that short and ineffectual distance? I doubt if anyone knows, though it may be a matter of smell, the snapper exuding something like musk, of which a little is perfume and a lot is a skunk!

Our gear was in the boat and we were ready to leave. It was a short trip to the end of Long Key where the reefs lay thick and snappers roamed in shoals, prowling like a wolf pack. We were going because a scientist from Philadelphia had come to the Keys to investigate the presence and nature of malignant tumors among the cold-blooded vertebrates of the sea. Cancer is a disease that afflicts all kinds of backboned animals and not merely mice and men. I have seen malignant tumors of the kidneys in many of the green frogs of Eastern Canada and New England, and one of the big turtles in the pound at Key West had a large tumor in its arm-pit. Gray snappers have them too, a kind that generally appears as a swelling on one side above the fore-fin. Only one or two snappers in a school would be likely to show them, and even at that the percentage is relatively a high one. The problem this June morning was to find a gray snapper with such a swelling and to catch the fish without killing it, an enterprise demanding more brain than brawn. It is almost impossible to take a snapper with a hook and line; and with a seine only one at a time is generally caught. There is no reason why it should be the right one.

For fish the gray snappers seem to be unusually intelligent. If you walk along the beach in the evening the snappers parallel your course, not because of any affinity for humanity but for a taste for ghost crabs. The crabs, scared by footsteps, scuttle into the water, the fish make a quick rush and the crabs are no more. I wondered how we would outwit our victim, even if we were lucky enough to spot one with a tumor.

The boat reached shallow water among the reefs and before not too long was drifting over a group of a dozen or more gray snappers. Luck was with us, for one of them did have an obvious swelling a little behind the head, and our Philadelphian said he wanted it. Very gently, the fisherman maneuvered the boat almost directly over the particular fish, and then, very, very gently, a cartridge of dynamite on the end of a wire was lowered into the water until it was level with the fish and a couple of feet to one side. Battery contact was made, the charge exploded and the stunned and outwitted but undamaged fish floated to the surface and was brought inboard.

The rest of the fish scattered but soon reformed their school and continued their prowl along the reef where the brightly colored reef fish drifted in and out of the coral caverns.

Suddenly they scattered again. A shadowy wraith, appearing like a ghost fish, had been hovering a little way offshore. No one had noticed it. Now it was driving like a battle cruiser for the terrified group of snappers—a barracuda at full speed, the most dangerous fish in the sea! And the hardest to see, haunting the lagoons like a lone tiger stalking silently through the dark jungle.

The barracuda herds its prey. Maybe it is because it can eat and digest just so many snappers at a time and likes to keep the next meal close to hand, or perhaps just because it enjoys the savage and bloodthirsty game for its own sake. Whatever the reason, the herded fish huddle together in abject fear, and a four-foot barracuda has been seen herding a school of about one hundred and fifty large gray snappers, not to mention innumerable yellow-tails, parrot fish, grunts, angel fish and cock-eyed pilots.

The cowering mob was in danger and each individual knew it, yet somehow each one seemed to recognize that its chances were better within the crowd than in making a conspicuous and lonely dash for freedom. Possibly the vibrating, forked tail of the barracuda, like the twitch and slow lash of the tail of a crouched tiger, had a hypnotic effect that froze time into eternity.

Barracudas rarely grow longer than six feet, but even a three-foot barracuda is more to be feared by fish or man than any shark. Most sharks are scavengers, many are cowards, and even the tiger shark has a mild disposition compared with a barracuda's. As a rule when an uninjured man falls overboard any nearby shark departs in a panic. But a barracuda, large or small, is inquisitive, utterly fearless and of an implacable temper. It is like a great pike and it launches itself at its prey in a fury, chopping and slicing off parts of a size it can readily swallow. The savage jaws carry sharp, strong, pointed teeth—truly fangs—that act as a buzz saw at the speed at which their

owner travels. When the teeth break off, which is neither unusual nor unexpected considering their use, the old roots are
resorbed and new teeth erupt to take their place.

Barracudas are probably responsible for most shark horror-
stories, and even a small one can be extremely dangerous to
a swimmer, for whom a severed artery can lead to quick death
in the sea. West Indian Negroes, often as much at home in
the water as on land, pay little attention to sharks but clamber
out in a crazed panic whenever the cry of "couter!" is raised.

The snappers began to go about their business again, minus
one in the boat and one in the barracuda, but they seemed to
keep an uneasy wariness, and you felt that while they were
looking for coral fish their minds were looking back over their
shoulders. There was no doubt the snappers were haunted by
the same fear we sometimes feel, when walking alone in the
dark countryside, that some unknown menace was following
behind and getting closer. But the fish couldn't laugh it off!

I could not help but wonder about the difference in color
of the gray snapper and the vivid coral fishes. Both were prey
to hunters, and gray seemed a good color to be if you have
to live out in the open among the barracudas, both as an effort
at camouflage and a reflection of your state of mind. But if
color is a camouflage, do the brightly-painted colors on the
reef fish, advertising their presence, suggest a lack of fear? Do
they say, in effect, "We don't taste good, don't bother to eat
us, silly," or "You can't catch us anyway among these corals
so we can wear any colors we like!" A biologist at Loggerhead
Key tried to find out. . . .

The warning-color theory does imply that the colorful reef

fish are distasteful. In one experiment, locally common sardines that snappers are accustomed to eat were dyed red. It made no difference and the snappers ate them readily. But when pieces of jellyfish tentacle, which sting like a nettle, were placed in the mouths of the sardines, the snappers very soon learned to avoid them and made no attempt to eat them for weeks. So the snapper can learn quickly enough, although he is not merely put off by bright colors. The fact is that coral fish are eaten whenever they can be caught, and they survive in spite of their colors. It is their habit of hiding in the crevices and grottoes of the coral where the snapper cannot follow that keeps them safe. If color does not give them security, what do the bright colors mean? The answer is hard to find and there is only this suggestion—that here is the real nature of Evolution—something new comes to the surface because it does not bring danger with it. The reef fish survives.

The tide was high and the reefs now lay covered by several feet of water. It was a good chance to watch the smaller fish darting in and out among the coral branches and sea-fans, to follow the blue heads and red squirrels, yellow grunts, slippery dicks and red cardinals as they went about their serious business of eating and avoiding being eaten. Lemon-yellow butterfly fish seemed almost to flutter as they shot quickly about, showing the black bar across their head and eyes and the large, black spot at the base of their tail. In fact they gave the impression of facing the wrong way, for the tail-spot looked more like an eye than the eye did, a bold stroke of camouflage indeed. At times they even wriggle backwards to increase the illusion, though ready to streak the other way in a split second.

Not all reef fish are small and lovely. Down among the holes under the coral heads of the reef lives a fish that looks less dangerous than it is—the moray eel. When a moray is hooked and pulled into a boat the fisherman usually gets out in a hurry. If the barracuda is the tiger of the sea the moray is more the serpent, with its long, thick, green or banded body, lying in wait for some luckless passer-by. Its small head has sharp wicked teeth and short, strong jaws, and the eel matches the barracuda in nasty disposition. It is always angry, vicious and aggressive, and the moral is that you should keep away from any dark hole among the reefs. Nothing lives in there that is the better for being disturbed. Even a normally timid octopus will react if stepped upon.

By now we were drifting along the edge of the reef where the water dropped into blue and short weed clung to the rocks. Flashes of wonderful color shot here and there, and then some came closer to the surface, parrot fish nibbling and scraping the velvety vegetation off the rocks with their parrot-like jaws. In places you could see the marks left on the rocks where the teeth had scraped. Their large size undoubtedly gave them a degree of safety. Anyway, they were browsing along the steeper slopes of the reef, unconcernedly flaunting their well-fed beauty encased in enormous scales of red, green or blue. Yet they did have an easy way of slipping unobtrusively out of sight with no loss of regality.

The sun was climbing high and the heat increased. It was time to take the tumorous snapper back to Loggerhead if it was to be of any use. So the boat was turned and the engine started. Startled by the sudden noise a number of small gars broke surface and shot a few feet into the air. They are curious, needle-like fish, with long slender jaws which lock together to make a fine spear. Sharp canines make the spear's head, and gars will dart at other fish to transfix and hold them. At times this habit can be more than a nuisance. Low tides at night are usually lower than day tides and afford the best collecting. And night collectors using lights on the reef have occasionally been seriously hurt by the needle-nosed gars driving for the light and puncturing the more-or-less naked human body.

As we returned to the laboratory, passing along the east side of Loggerhead where the turtle grass grew thick in the shallows, large conch, among the largest marine snails in the world, were feeding among the weed. Probably you have seen the shells of these whelks ornamenting the homes of some of your more antique relatives. They have other uses too, apart from their domestic value to the mollusk. Fishermen chip off the point of the shell to make a hole, and the conch is blown as a horn which can be heard as far away as a bugle, and is just as hard to blow.

I wondered if the conch below sheltered the same little fish as those among the Marquesas reefs not far away. On one occasion when conch were being collected, one of those tossed into the boat landed mouth upward and stayed that way with the shell still full of water. The men in the boat were startled to see small pink cardinal fish swimming about in the cavity between the shell and the mollusk. It was no accidental catch, for investigation showed the conch to be the regular home of this little fish. But other questions remain to be answered.

Is the fish of any benefit to the conch, can it come and go at will, when does it feed, does it stick to one host, how close to home does it stay, and how does it breed? We can guess only at the last, for its close relative, the scarlet cardinal of the coral heads, carries the eggs in its mouth until they are hatched.

It is a curious association and it makes you realize that for countless years these animals of the reefs and lagoons must have been living close together. Perhaps the slender little pearl fishes have gone to the extreme in large sea cucumbers, relatives of the sea urchin and starfish which are common around the keys of the Tortugas and are easily caught. If you place one or two in a pail of sea-water and leave them until the water becomes a little stagnant, you find suddenly that the pail contains pearl fish as well as cucumbers. They slip tail first into the cloacal opening of the cucumbers and can come and go at will, and use these echinoderms as shelter even more intimately than the cardinals do the conch.

The boat drew alongside the dock, the water looked cool and inviting, and there was no sign of barracuda. Only the man with the snapper had work to do.

CHAPTER SEVEN

CRABS AND SPONGES

FROM Loggerhead you can see the clearcut edge of the sea all around you except to the north, where the other Keys run together in a thin line beyond the lagoon. On Loggerhead there is a lighthouse and a Carnegie Laboratory. It takes all of three minutes to go from one to the other, along the avenue of short coconut palms. I timed it. And if you are determined to take a long, brisk walk, you can plod steadily and slowly through the soft beach sand around the entire island in twenty minutes.

The enchanted isle, sanctuary and relief from noise and tension as it is when you first land there, can become a prison unless you are free to leave it at will until, finally, the few days before the boat returns to Key West can seem interminable. It was during these days that the crabs and I got acquainted. Land crabs and land hermits scuttled among the low thick shade of sea grape and sesuvium where I walked, and at night the ghost crabs came out of their burrows and darted swiftly across the sand between the tides.

Spiders are animals that have always bothered me. They move fast and I do not enjoy their close company; and while crabs are very different from spiders, the one recalls the other. Crabs in cool, northern waters demand respect, to be sure, but even the largest do not move too fast and there is usually time enough for both parties to avoid mutual embarrassment.

In the tropics it is a very different matter. Birds, human beings and their relatives in the rest of the hairy tribe are all constantly warm-blooded. If anything, they find it more difficult to keep busy in the heat than in the cold. It is otherwise with those of cold blood, whose body heat is neither more nor less than the air or water around them. When it is hot, all the activities and chemical reactions of their bodies are fast, when it is cold they are slow. Now the speedup when the temperature changes from the sixties and seventies of a Maine shore to the high nineties of the sun-baked rocks in the tropics is for most of these animals a matter of from four- to six-fold. If you will translate this into terms of movement you will begin to get the idea. . . .

A green crab scuttling mistakenly in your direction on a Cape Cod beach can do about two feet in a second if it really tries. In bare feet I wouldn't argue with it even at that, for a crab needn't be big to pinch hard. But if the crab were one of those long-legged, red-and-yellow monstrosities of the South traveling at ten feet per second, probably making a frantic dash for the safety of the sea or a crevice, no amount of common sense can prevent, in the human male who happens to be in its way, the birth of a neurosis. Now I know why some women climb chairs when they see a mouse.

Most crabs can run around out of water for awhile, though most of them sooner or later will keel over and die. Even then they have done better than most sea animals could have. Some stand it out of water much better than others, and of those on the Tortugas three or four are among the best of their kind.

Hermit crabs of course have an initial out-of-water advantage in their use of empty snail shells as portable houses, for while in the sea the shells serve mainly to protect their soft and vulnerable rears, on land they provide a moist chamber that helps keep the crab from drying up. This is not enough in itself, and few hermits really take kindly to being left out of water. There is the matter of breathing. Oxygen is still essential and the problem is to take it from the air, instead of from the water, as is the usual practice.

Crab gills are covered by a shield of the hard outer body covering to keep them from damage, and clean water is bailed incessantly through the gill chambers. The feathery, spongy gills take up most of the chamber space. While the animal is submerged water can be made to flow through them easily. Out of water it is difficult to drive air through them and the crab soon asphyxiates. How is it then, that some crabs, hermits and others, manage to live out of water and even to flourish? One hermit, in fact, has lost its shell and hardened its rear, and lives for the most part in the tops of coconut palms. It may not move very quickly, but any crab that can husk a coconut and crack its shell should be admired and let well alone. You get the feeling it was a smart crab to discover coconuts in the first place, particularly since it must be a crab with a certain amount of forethought that stores coconuts in his burrow to be eaten during the off-season. But when you think of it, the real feat was to leave the sea and live happily in the top of a palm tree. Why aren't we as impressed, if not actually as dumbfounded, as we would be if it were say, a monkey that had left the tree top to play tag with an octopus beneath the sea? It's much the same thing in reverse.

How do they do it? On the Tortugas keys there are four land crabs, all with close relatives living below the edge of the tide, so that comparisons have been possible. There are the land hermit crab and the ghost crab, and two other land crabs related to two kinds of tidal crabs. In all of these, as compared with their water-dwelling cousins, the number and size of the gills have become greatly reduced, allowing the gill chamber to serve as a lung chamber to an efficient extent, yet retaining sufficient gill tissue for the animal to get along well enough under water. When you consider further that the crabs as a group, because of their hard outer case, dry out less readily than any other kinds of animals except some snails, it is not surprising that they are inclined to leave the sea and shore-line to exploit what food and safety may lie above the high tide. Yet like the turtle tied to the land, they remain prisoners, only chained to the sea as closely as frogs to a pond and for the same reason. In both cases the adults can live more or less happily on the land. In neither case can the eggs hatch out of water. When the time for breeding comes around, the land crabs and land hermits alike return to the sea to shed their young. How many succeed in regaining their sanctuary above the tide, nobody knows.

Ghost crabs and their ubiquitous fiddler cousins seem to have had some difficulty in making up their collective racial mind just where they belong, in the water or out. They burrow just out of reach of the tide, yet the ghost crab cannot live altogether out of water for more than a day. Fiddlers do better and can live freely in or out of water for as long as six weeks at a time. Otherwise the two crabs are much alike and they have worked out their own little ways of life between the wind and rain of the land, and the frothing fringe of the sea.

They construct oblique burrows, as long as three feet, that usually end in a horizontal room. They dig by packing the wet sand between their legs and carapace, and then press it into pellets which are carefully removed from the burrow. You can generally tell a new burrow by the little mound of sand pellets piled in front of the opening. Sometimes hours are spent in making the end room, the depth of which is determined by how far the fiddler must go to reach sand that is very moist but not exactly wet.

The burrow is usually lined with mud, and before each high tide the crab plugs the entrance, managing to live comfortably in a fairly airtight and watertight compartment in a moist climate perfect for its needs. There is no question of memorizing the tidal rhythm, which would be a complicated affair—each rising tide simply moistens the air chamber before it reaches the opening of the burrow, and the crab immediately becomes active and carries pellets to build a door. If it is taken by surprise and finds water seeping in without previous warning, it rushes to the entrance and pulls pellets inside in great haste without taking time to make a door.

Divers go down into the sea with an air tube or oxygen supply of some sort, taking their gaseous oxygen with them into the world of water. The fiddlers apparently do just the opposite. Their gills can get oxygen only from sea-water, and so they keep them submerged in portable sea-water within the gill chambers all the time they are on land. They only go into the sea long enough to replenish it and must be looked upon as true water-breathers living on land, just as the turtle is an air-breather in the sea.

It was a pity there were no fiddlers about on the keys (though they would be common enough on the beaches to the north) for fiddlers have a trick that seems out of this world. Young fiddlers of either sex have a pair of small claws, and females retain them that way for all their lives. In the males the right claw grows to an enormous size, so that most of the time he seems to be bowing a fiddle. Now, should the large claw be lost, a common enough accident, the little claw of the left side grows into a new large one, and a new small claw grows on the right where the large claw used to be, making Willy the Fiddler left handed. The ghost crab cannot do this, though it can regenerate whichever claw is missing, without reversal.

The fiddler crabs are not alone in being able to switch their right to their left. Alpheus, the pistol crab, can do as much, although it is more like a baby lobster than a true crab, not unlike a shrimp except for the claws. These little changelings lived close at hand on Loggerhead, though you would never know it unless you knew their habits. Then you might find ten thousand all at once.

The pistol crab is a fascinating little brute in its own right. Like the fiddler, it has one large claw and one small claw, but where the fiddler waves his big claw aloft in a mood of sexual exhibitionism, the pistol crab lives up to his name in another way. Keep one in a glass jar of water, and every now and then it will snap its big claw against the glass with a sharp noise that can be heard a hundred feet away. Even without the glass the snapping is considerable, though what the sound means in the world of Alpheus nobody knows. Considering the uproar ten thousand pistol crabs could raise if the spirit moved them, it is just as well that the sponge (where they live, and as many as this in one sponge) has no recognizable nervous system. It would be a shattering experience to have all that happen inside you. It is only since the war, as asdic detectors have come into use for fish locating, that we are beginning to realize what a diversity of odd noises marine animals make in the ocean and on the seafloor, sounds that may have their special mysterious meanings—or like much other sound and fury signifying nothing.

Pistol crabs have been famous for a long time but not because of the clamor they make. Their story goes back to Vienna, at the time of the Empire and the waltz, from there to North Carolina, and thence to the Dry Tortugas. Pzribram in Vienna and Wilson at Beaufort, N. C., discovered that when both the large *and* the small claws are removed at their natural breaking joints, large and small claws grow anew in their proper places. ("Breaking joints" are where injured legs or claws are normally snapped off by a crab to prevent bleeding to death.) When only the large claw is removed, the small claw of the opposite side grows into a large one. It is the same as the fiddler, although repeating a mystery doesn't solve it, but merely emphasizes it. The point is that pistol crabs and fiddlers both perform the mirror trick although the ghost crab, which is more closely related to the fiddler, cannot. We find the same sort of thing among worms. There is a group of marine worms that reside in calcareous tubes of their own making, attached to rocks. One end of the worm sticks out like a brightly colored flower, with two sets of highly decorative tentacles. On one side only, one tentacle has a conical knob at its end, and when the worm withdraws into its tube the knob is the last to be pulled in, fitting the end of the tube like a cork. Its opposite number is a tiny, abortive tentacle with not much to do. But if the knob-tentacle is damaged or lost, the small, hitherto useless tentacle grows up into a new one.

No one has yet thought of a good explanation, though quite a number have been eliminated. In the case of the pistol crab some experiments carried out at Loggerhead add a little more information which may serve as a further clue. The small claw begins to change into a large claw at the first molt after the original large claw has been removed, just as soon as growth of any sort can take place in the animal as a whole. But if, at the time the large claw is removed, some legs of the other side are lost, the small claw of that side no longer grows and the unhappy crab soon finds itself with a pair of small claws, one on each side. This sort of thing goes to the roots of nature—if we understood it we would also know a lot about much else that is still a mystery.

Not only the crabs, but the sponges too throw in their bit to make matters not only more interesting but more confusing. If you take a live sponge and break it up, then slowly force the pieces through bolting silk (a strong, finely meshed cloth used in flour-manufacture) into sea-water, the sponge tissues separate into their constituent cells. After a while the isolated cells settle on the bottom of the dish where they make a thick film. Leave the dish overnight. By morning, the film is gone and in its place are numerous tiny islands of cells. By some means the cells have moved about and become stuck together in groups. Nothing further seems to happen unless they are kept healthy for two or three weeks. Then you find that most of the small pieces have become minute sponges with all of a sponge's delicate organization and structure. And should the cells of two different kinds of sponges be mixed up together in the suspension, the chances are that they will sort themselves out so that each small new sponge will be one kind or the other, but not a mixture.

It is no wonder that new sponges grow where old sponges have been torn off. Sponges are one animal that cannot be exterminated by overfishing, although sponges of marketable size and quality may be easily over-collected. Disease is a much more deadly enemy than man, for a change.

Divers descend for sponges in the warm waters of the Gulf Coast and the Bahamas, and in the eastern Mediterranean, often with little protection against the pressure of deep water. If you visit Tarpon Springs on the Gulf coast of Florida you will see how the East has come to the West—almost every fishing boat drawn up alongside the sponge market carries a Greek name and has lines unfamiliar in the Western world.

Among the shallow waters and reefs of the Bahamas sponges are actually farmed. They are cut up and the pieces are wired firmly to cement blocks and planted in the lagoons. After a few years each piece is a well-formed sponge that can be dried, bleached and sold. Even in these days of synthetic substitutes a use for the real thing lingers on.

The great Loggerhead Sponges grow below the tide, from shallow water to the bottom of the lagoon—sponges like huge, dark vases, holding as much as twenty-five gallons. These are not the kind whose dried skeletons serve to scrub humanity, even if they do share with those and most other living sponges the grand prize for the vilest smells in creation. There is even a small, rough, slate-colored reef sponge about the size of your hand, common along the lee-side of Bird Key reef, whose personal name is "foetida," which emphasizes that even for a sponge it has an evil smell!

Loggerhead sponges live long and grow large, and have a maze of innumerable channels in their tissues through which sea-water continually flows. For any animals which are small enough, though not so small the sponge cells can feed upon them, these channels and cavities are a perfect sanctuary. And what the sponge draws in through its pores they can feed on too.

It was less difficult to find one of these large sponges than it was for us to get it into a washtub and carry it ashore. As other collectors have found before, the sponge was literally crawling with a host of small lodgers, not exactly parasites since they did not feed on the sponge tissue itself. Several hundred barnacles held tightly to the outer surface, as though it were to a rock. And within the spongy matrix of the thick walls three other kinds of animals abounded. There must have been well over a hundred thin, wriggling little marine worms, and as far as I could ascertain without spending two or three days of tedious counting, there were about 9,000 pistol crabs, each about an inch long. And of these about one in twenty carried a queer crustacean parasite on its own gills. Of course there were other organisms, but they were few or small, except for some that were entangled among the anchoring roots at the base of the vase. Here were several palolo worms, a sea urchin, a crab or two, a conch and a basket star. When you think of it, only fish were missing, and if we had been more careful a few small cardinals might have been caught swimming within.

There is no doubt at all—a single Loggerhead sponge is a world in itself, an animal community, an ecological unit as definite as a coral reef.

CHAPTER EIGHT

THE SANDS OF TIME

THE warm Gulf water sweeps up the Atlantic coast, pressing against the shelf of our continent in a lingering caress before it swings to the east on its long drift to Northern Europe. As if they would hook it to our land, the two great Capes, Hatteras and Cod, reach out into the sea with sprawling, shoaling banks of sand thrusting below the waters, fingers of the shore that shift and writhe with the race of the currents.

Small wonder that the first settlers found themselves on the northern sides of the Capes where the south-bound countercurrents brought them inshore, the Pilgrims finding the cold, bleak course to Cape Cod, the Virginians steering toward the sun and landing along the sand-spits north of Hatteras. Luck was with them both, for the Cape sands are wrecking sands that have brought disaster to many a ship.

The same sands can make it difficult for a biologist to find any sea life along these Capes that is not a sand-dweller. But where the sand gives way to a solid footing you'll find it exploited enough, and my Atlantic coast-crawl, starting at the Dry Tortugas, found me two seasons later 800 miles north, at Beaufort Island, N. C., at high tide an island no bigger than Loggerhead Key, where I found a small marine-life laboratory which had been established by a few enterprising biologists from the University of North Carolina at about the same time as the Tortugas laboratory.

My work was to be a study of the life cycles of hydroids that give rise to jellyfish, a study which at one point became quite personally first-hand, or should I say first-arm? One evening, when the full moon was rising, I slipped into the gently cooling water for an evening swim and a closer examination of the blue-black sea squirts, tunicates that fastened themselves to the pilings of the Beaufort Island Bridge. The current was a little strong and I had to hang on with an arm around one of these barnacle-encrusted posts. Suddenly the arm began to tingle as if I had grabbed a load of nettles. Something very small was stinging, and even had I known in advance that the pilings were covered with a feathery growth of hydroids I would have been just as careless, for while I knew they sting and feed upon tiny swimming organisms, I also knew the human skin is pretty tough and the nettle cells of hydroids can rarely get through. These got through all right, and they demanded more attention than my sea squirts. But it was almost worth it, for as I looked closely at the pilings and the water around I could see thousands of minute pink jellyfish, each no more than one-eighth of an inch across and already fully-laden with eggs or sperm. They were breaking off every second from the hydroids that had grown them, launching into the current of high tide to sow their seed before dawn.

When the tide is low around Beaufort you can walk for miles along the wet, flat sands that the outer currents have thrown in behind the dune-islands lying south of Hatteras Light. Tempting tracks in this expanse of wet sand can lead you on for a hundred yards at a time, before they come to their sudden ends and invite an exploratory digging hand. One such track, a broad smudge trail that rarely lasted for more than a few yards, usually ended with at least some visible sign of its maker—a flip of the finger and out came a sand dollar.

You'll find sand dollars along sandy shores from Maine to Mexico and California, flat, more-or-less circular discs covered with a felty coat of small, close-packed spines. They are, perhaps fortunately for them, not as negotiable in banking circles as their fiscal namesake. The wonder is that they can make a track of any kind—few animals look less animated and less capable of locomotion. Yet they do move, and they are, dollar-like, adept at disappearing before your eyes.

Sand dollars and sea biscuits are worth looking at a little closely. Hold them obliquely and you can see light shimmering across the surface as waves of rippling action over the spines. The mouth lies at the center of the flat under surface and you can see the white tips of five teeth poking through it. Break open a dead shell and the teeth look like five little birds.

Look along the edge of a dollar. A small hole is the anus, and its position suggests that the opposite edge is where the head ought to be, only it isn't. There is none. And on the topside center you'll see five petals, delicate leaf-shaped traceries reaching halfway out to the edge. Tiny filamentous fingers extend through the petals into the water and enable the dollar to breathe—despite its lack of a brain, eyes and legs, it's still an animal with all of an animal's need for oxygen. In season it sends out clouds of microscopic eggs or sperm through five pores where the petals come together, to mix with the ocean currents and eventually make more sand dollars.

These I found were keyhole dollars that move faster than

D

most. Slits like keyholes pass through the body of the disc and their function becomes clear as you watch the animal gliding along. Sand stirred up by the locomotory under surface comes up through the slits and on to the upper surface, to fall eventually off behind. The result keeps the animal covered with a thin layer of sand as it goes on its travels, so that a passing gull or fish might overlook it, though few creatures could offer more unappetizing discomfort and less nourishment.

Other sand dollars have less symmetry and no slits, and are less able to move about, although they can submerge in the sand beyond the reach of a marauding starfish with astonishing rapidity. There is a west-coast dollar that lives in remarkably closely packed communities, in one instance as many as 468 individuals being found in a single square yard. These lie flat on the sand when the tide leaves them, but in still water stand on edge with about two-thirds of their disc buried. If there is a current the whole bed of dollars leans away from it at a uniform angle.

Farther along I found a pen shell, a handsome, fragile thing shaped like a fan whose thin, open ends can cut your feet badly. It was the only one I saw with the animal still alive and its "byssus" threads intact. These anchoring threads, fine and greenish-gold as a mermaid's hair might be, have made the animal famous. From ancient times in the Mediterranean the threads have been woven into the glamorous cloth-of-gold of the medieval world. You can still, in Taranto, buy souvenir garments made of it.

But the long trails usually lead not to the dollars, but to young horseshoe crabs. Nothing can generally be seen at the

end of a meandering 100-foot track until a poke with your
finger brings to light a little sand-colored Limulus from one
to several inches long. Only occasionally at Beaufort did I see
the dark, massively-armored adults stranded on the beach by
receding tides.

Now I find it difficult to think of any animal less beautiful
than the horseshoe crab, and while many are much more repulsive in their own way, Limulus has not only a bizarre attraction, but its fantastic antiquity is a world-wide object of
inquiry.

In spite of its grotesque appearance the animal is utterly
harmless to everything but worms and small clams. The great
shield that covers its body is purely defensive, like the shell of
a turtle, while the long dangerous-looking spine projecting
from its rear simply serves to right the animal when a wave or
a fish, or its own clumsiness, turns it on its back. Unless Limulus can stick the point of its spine into the sand, it can no
more turn itself over again than you can change a tire without a jack. Almost all its life is spent grubbing along submerged sand flats, feeding on such small, soft animals as it can
find. When young, the whole horseshoe shield may be below
the surface of the sand, but the two-foot-long adult is too thick
for this and the upper part of the protective dome remains
exposed, though the flange along the edge of the shield is kept
buried, partly to act as a plow but also to prevent currents and
waves from driving beneath the animal and rolling it over.
And so the eyes are placed where they serve best, in the top
of the shield, facing upward and outward, one on each side
and a third one middle and front, even though the optic
nerves have to pass through the so-called liver to reach that

apology for a brain which surrounds the mouth.

If you find a Limulus, a most likely event between the Capes where they are so common that they are misused for fertilizer and chicken feed, you should turn it over on its back in shallow water. Its efforts at righting itself are interesting enough, but it is also worthwhile looking at the underneath side rather closely, for the complex series of appendages constitute a beautiful piece of machinery, beautiful, that is, in the sense of functional fitness, like a combustion engine. When the animal relaxes from its inept effort to roll itself up into a ball like a pill bug or like the extinct Trilobites, an effort which is thwarted by the fact that the horseshoe crab now has only two hinges of the many it used to have, the whole mechanism is set into rhythmic motion. The nervous discharge which is responsible for it all starts at the front and sweeps down to the tail. First to move is the pair of small pincers in front of the mouth, innocuous equivalents of the poison fangs of a spider and the great brandishing claws of a scorpion. Next in motion are the five pairs of legs. They look like the legs of a crab but they are not—Limulus is not a crab. Each leg has a broad grinding surface at its base, and the five pairs of bases act like molars and grind up the food, shoving it into the mouth that lies between. It is a queer state of affairs, but the animal has to chew as it walks and walk as it chews, and can never settle down to a quiet meal. Eat or rest it may, but never at the same time.

Now this manner of walking itself is peculiar. The action of the five pairs of ordinary legs merely lifts the cumbersome body off the ground. They do not actually "walk," as do those of a crab or a lobster. The forward movement comes from the powerful thrusting action of a sixth pair, longer and stronger than the others. As the first five lift up the body as though it were poised on stilts, the remaining pair push down and backwards and the animal lurches violently forward. It is the same thrust that a skier gets from his ski poles when he pushes from a standing start, and if you closely examine the pushers of Limulus you see the ski-pole structure exactly, a shaft ending in a spike which is prevented by spreading flaps from sinking too far into the soft ground. The pushing legs thrust only after the front pairs have acted and the body is lifted.

Your Limulus is still on his back—the nervous impulse has now reached the hind part of the body, the abdomen, and the five pairs of gill-books wave rhythmically and expose their closely packed leaves to the oxygen in the water. Each "book" contains up to a hundred thin parchment-like respiratory leaves—hence the name. And so, a single rippling discharge from the nerve center produces a feeding and mastication reaction, a unique lurching kind of locomotion, and the breathing movements of gill-books which may even enable the animal to swim.

Living horseshoes can be found most readily along the edge of the sea when the tide is out. You may think you see them on the sand above the high water mark, as we did another time walking along Pleasant Bay on the outer elbow of Cape Cod. Hundreds seemed to be crowded together with wave-tossed weed and wind drift. They were all about six inches long, a definite age group, probably in their third summer. Yet when we went to pick them up it was obvious that they were neither alive nor even dead—they weren't home, and only empty cases covered the beach, light and airy or partly filled with sand. At first I thought the insides had disintegrated, but the slit along the broad front edge of the shield showed what had happened. They were molts. The hard outer case has to be cast off periodically for the animal to grow, and the cast shells of the two- or three-year-olds in the bay had drifted ashore to be tossed up by the wind and tide. Probably the molts of the one-year and the four- and five-year-olds would have been found at another time or in different parts of the bay.

Full-grown individuals only come into the region between the tides during the breeding season in early summer. Then, when the moon is full and the tides run highest, the large female comes ashore at the high tide, heavy with eggs, to dig a hole in the sand. One or several males come with her, often riding on her back, in fact, and when the hole is dug only a small part of the back of the male lying on top of the female can be seen. Eggs and milt are deposited in the hole and buried, and each nest usually contains about ten thousand greenish-blue translucent eggs about a twelfth of an inch in diameter. They hatch after a month and come out more or less like the parent except for the lack of a tail spine.

But the fascination of Limulus for zoologists is not his queer person itself, nor is it because physiologists have delved deep into the nature of its blue blood, its beating heart, or its vision. It lies rather in the questions it raises of time, space and change—questions that are hard to answer but will not be ignored.

Limulus can be found on the Atlantic coast from the Gulf of Maine to the Gulf of Mexico, even as far as Yucatan, with the greatest numbers in Long Island Sound and at the mouth of the Delaware River. It also lives abundantly among the famed Spice Islands of the eastern Indian Ocean, and in lesser numbers in nearby waters. If you look at a map of the world or a globe that shows the ocean currents, warm and cold, and the depth of the seas, you can see what this means, and why zoologists whose concern it is to figure out how animals have come to be what they are, *where* they are, are inclined to stay awake at night.

For horseshoe crabs, whether newborn or fully grown, are no travelers. They hug the sea floor, move about with difficulty, and end their lives within a few miles of the place of their birth. They are among the least effective swimmers in the sea. Yet going from west to east, the American Limulus is separated from its Asiatic brothers by the whole expanse of the North and South Atlantic and the Indian Ocean, about 12,000 miles of water, some three miles deep. From east to west, 7,000 miles of the even-deeper Pacific and the whole American continent itself lie in between. Limulus certainly did not crawl or swim from one region to the other, no matter how many generations may have lived and died during the journey, unless the world was very different from what it is now.

So we come to the question—if the migration from one place to the other, or to both places from somewhere in between, could only have happened some time in the distant past, how long a fabulous past has Limulus had during which this might have happened?

The answer is hardly believable. Fossils show that Limulus has existed as Limulus for practically two hundred million years. Whether the estimate in years is accurate or not, it goes back to the Triassic period, long before the time of the first birds or the hairy mammals, or the bees and butterflies and flowers. It has lived on sand or mud flats somewhere in the seas without undergoing any recognizable change all through the immensity of time that the life and vegetation of the land we know best has taken to come into being. And if we extend the name of Limulus to include older types so similar that only experts can tell the difference, we push its existence on this planet almost twice as far back as that, to a time before life of any kind, plant or animal, lived out of water. Here the doors to speculation open wide.

Now, one of the reasons European zoologists are so interested in Limulus when they have never seen it alive or even dead is that fine fossils of Limulus are commonly found in Bavaria, north of the Alps. While not the oldest rocks to be sure, for they are of the Upper Jurassic Period, no more than one hundred and thirty million years old, they still furnish another piece of the puzzle, and one that must be fitted. Remember that the highest mountains are the youngest, and that the mountain chains that comprise the Himalayas and the Alps, and the whole western edge of the American continents are new in the life of Limulus, however old they may be to man.

Warm and ancient seas once swept over Bavaria, seas that were part of a great sea that extended across what is now India and the Himalayas, to sweep west and north over central Europe to the North Sea. Geologists call it the Sea of Tethys, and the Mediterranean and the Black and Caspian Seas are all that remain of it. But along the shores of that Bavarian Sea of the Upper Jurassic, Limulus went ashore to lay its eggs when the tides were high, flying reptiles launched themselves over the sea from the cliffs, forerunners of the pterodactyls, with their 20-foot wing-spread, of a later age. While in the forests not far from this ancient sea, ten-inch "pre-butterflies" and fourwinged birds with long tails and clawed fingers glided between the trees. It was the end of an epoch and the beginning of the modern world.

This brings Limulus from the East Indies to the Atlantic coast of Europe, but it still leaves the American group isolated by the Atlantic and Pacific Oceans. Geologists tell us however that the Isthmus of Panama has broken several times, and not too long ago. What difference does this make? Specimens of Limulus that were transplanted from the shores of Maryland to San Francisco Bay grew to large size but never reproduced their kind—the water was too cold. But with the breaking of the Isthmus to any considerable depth, the warm north Equatorial current that pours westward across the tropical Atlantic from the Bight of Africa into the Caribbean and the Gulf of Mexico, and now comes out again as our Gulf Stream, would continue its course into the Pacific. It is difficult to say what must have happened, but its impact would have played havoc with a system of currents such as now exist in that ocean, and it is possible that the whole shoreline of a warm north Pacific from Indo-China to Central America was a playground for Limulus. With the closing of the Isthmus and the opening of the Bering Straits, cold water from the depths and from the north killed them off. It is a possible explanation, yet it is unlikely.

One more remains. There are rocks in Maryland which are magnetized in a way that could have occurred only in the southern hemisphere. Either the interpretation given by modern physicists is incorrect, or Maryland and at least a large part of the North American mainland at one time lay in the southern hemisphere and has since drifted to the north, or else the poles themselves have been shifting about. Our ideas of geography are as much in the melting pot as our knowledge of matter and energy has been, and somewhere in the confusing welter of sliding continents, swinging poles, the rising and falling of lands and the fusion of oceans, lies the enigma of the two communities of Limulus.

This is not quite all of it. Every zoologist is acutely aware of Limulus in another way altogether. It is simply the fact of Limulus the horseshoe crab in relation to ourselves—the contrast between one animal that has remained unchanged for hundreds of millions of years, and another, over the same period, that became a perfected terrestrial reptile and continued to transform gradually into a warm-blooded hairy mammal, bearing its young alive and suckling it, ascending to the treetops to evolve hands, eyes that can focus on them, a brain worth having, and a voice, at last to become a human biped creating symphonies and threatening its own extinction in atomic war. Where lies the secret of the drive to make a mind, and what does the ageless survival of an unchanging, mindless Limulus signify?

CHAPTER NINE

THE SAILOR AND THE CROSS

THROUGHOUT centuries the Passion of Christ has dominated the Christian World. It has been symbolized by man in the stars, in the Passion Flower, and in the skull of a catfish. You may have seen such a skull, belonging to the bewhiskered fish that frequents the muddy mouths of rivers where they enter the sea. It is a skull that has been known by many eras, by native Christians who have venerated it and by the Spanish and English sailors who found it in the days of the Spanish Main and their lust for gold. I came across it again around Pamlico Sound, near Beaufort.

This skull's under side, which is the roof of its owner's mouth, presents a perfect crucifix, complete with figure outstretched on the cross and halo behind its head. On the other side, the bones stand for the spear and breastplate of the Roman soldier and the toga of Pontius Pilate. When the skull is shaken, the "dice" are heard to rattle, like the dice the soldiers cast for the garments of the Lord. Other eyes, those of the 17th Century, saw the figure of a robed monk, with outstretched arms, in the bones of the upper side.

These are the symbols—what are the realities? The "cross" itself is the supporting architecture of the skull base—the long shaft of the cross underlying the brain and carrying the main burden, the shorter crossbar supporting the organs of balance. The "dice" are the pair of earstones lying within a bony box on each side of the hind brain and serving to balance, not to hear. All fish have them and, in a less compact form, so do all other backboned creatures from lizard to man. The stony weights press down upon sensory hairs which communicate by nerves with the brain, and as the fish moves, different hairs are touched as they come to lie beneath the weights. Thus gravity makes itself felt, and as the fish grows so do the earstones, slowly in winter, faster in summer, as annual growth rings are laid down which can be seen and counted, like the rings in a tree, to tell the fish's age.

The "halo" is something else again. The several small bones which make it up are found in many bony fishes and were long ago described by Max Weber, 19th Century German professor of comparative anatomy immortalized in the name of these bones, the Weberian ossicles. They are part of a long story, a sideline of our own past, and as we look at the bones we might pause to say, "there but for the grace of God go we," for the story goes back to a crisis in the history of evolving life —our kind of life in particular. . . .

The ancient bony fishes lived for the most part in the swamps and lakes of the coal forests of Devonian and Carboniferous times. Slowly the waters grew stagnant and some of the fish came to have lungs and took their oxygen from the air. Then came the parting of the ways. Some left the water altogether and started the tribe of four- and two-legged creatures that have plagued the earth ever since. Others drifted down to the sea, taking with them lungs no longer needed as the water improved.

So we come back to our catfish. An old lung has been retained as an airbladder, and with it, an air tube . . . and a
croak. It is that croak, incidentally, that has kept me interested
in catfish for a long time. A voice means nothing if it cannot
be heard, and to make it heard from one catfish to another,
the bony Weberian ossicles link the wall of the airbladder to
the back of the air sacs, and the vibrations pass through. So
far as we can tell, the catfish signal to one another by voice
through the muddy waters of their choice.

When we turn the skull over, more of the fish comes to light.
The robes of the monk are simply the large, heavy plate bones
protecting the brain and sense organs—so effectively that it is
almost impossible to kill a catfish by a blow on the head. The
breastplate bone is a little different. It serves to protect and
fasten the powerful neck muscles that give the fish much of its
strong swimming power. It also serves to guard the mechanism
of pulley muscles that operate the dorsal spine, for such is
our "spear." This spine can be raised or lowered by the action
of the muscles passing down the back of the skull, and a "nail
of the cross" acts as a stop to prevent it from tipping too far
forward.

Thus we come to the Sailor. The other name for the crucifix fish is the Gaff-Topsail Catfish, a true mariner's name if
ever there was one. Dictionaries define a gaff as "a spar extending the top of a fore-and-aft sail not set on stays," and the
sea catfish raises a great dorsal fin, like a topsail, when the
spine is pulled erect. This sail sometimes cuts the surface of
the water, though most of the time the fish swims close to the
bottom.

Apparently the first man to look at the whole catfish with

a seeing eye and mind was George Marcgrave, for in 1648 he described and pictured the sea cat in his *Natural History of Brazil,* noting that, "it has a beard made of four ray-like barbels, two of which are eight digits long and wide like straps, and two are short ones. To the dorsal fin there is (attached) a similar strap nine digits long, and behind the gill, barbels of the same kind." In the same century, writing a few decades later, Thomas Ash had this to say about the same fish, found off the coast of North Carolina—a "catfish, whose head and glaring eyes resemble a cat; it's esteemed a good fish. It hath a sharp thorny Bone on its Back, which strikes at such as endeavor to take it; which by seamen is held venemous; I saw one of our seamen, the back of whose hand was pierced with it, yet no poysonous symptoms of Inflammation or Rancor appeared on the Wound, which quickly healed, that I concluded it was either false or that of this Fish there were more kinds than one."

The sea catfish is in fact a subtropical form that ranges as far north as Cape Cod, but is particularly common along the South Atlantic and Gulf coasts. It is not surprising that biologists have taken notice of it. It is only surprising that we have taken so long to discover so little. The reason is mud. And though the fish is taken everywhere in the brackish estuaries of North Carolina, it took that indefatigable investigator, Dr. Eugene Gudger, now Curator of Fishes at the American Museum of Natural History, many years to discover the facts of catfish life.

What, for example, are the cat's whiskers? The alley cat travels by night through narrow places, as its ancestors prowled the bush or the jungle. Its whiskers are there to touch and to tell Kitty that a passage will permit its body to follow its head. Catfish whiskers are also for touch, but for taste as well. Imagine yourself if you possibly can, with slender processes extending from your tongue, hanging down from your mouth and trailing along the ground, and you begin to get the feeling a catfish does when its barbels touch some delicious morsel.

Nothing is known of the feeding habits of the sea catfish in nature, since the feeding grounds are either mud flats covered by water much too muddy to see through, or sandflats in water that is too deep. But in large aquaria in the marine laboratory at Beaufort, Gudger observed them swimming about with their long barbels just touching the bottom. When something edible was touched, there was a quick turn, a sudden opening of the cavernous mouth and it was gone. If bits of oyster were dropped into the aquarium and touched by the whiskers of a young fish, the fish would stop in full flight, so to speak, and even turn a somersault to get at it.

Another tale comes from Dr. Gudger, and it is one that tells as much about the tenacious nature of a naturalist as about the activities of catfish. One day in July, while out with a pound-net fisherman in Pamlico Sound, the naturalist found catfish eggs with young on them among the fish in the nets. The adult fish must have carried them and it could only mean that the eggs had developed within the body of the female after being fertilized internally, or that they were fertilized after extrusion and subsequently carried around in the mouth, as suggested by rumors and by knowledge of some catfish in other parts of the world. Thus commenced the long search for eggs and embryos, a search that lasted through the spring and summer of six years.

Fishermen swore that "the sea-cat spits its young out of its mouth," and that when the fish are struck on the head or thrown in the boats, the eggs would fly out of their mouths. So the following year an early start was made and females were caught which still had their eggs within the ovaries. Then in mid-June spent females were taken with no eggs either in ovaries or anywhere else. The breeding season was starting.

A few days later, fishmen and fishermen ("fishman" is just jargon for anyone who lives, breathes, and thinks fish) went to the Narrows of Newport River where the river proper enters the estuary. The tides there swirl around the oyster reefs at the edges of extensive mud flats, digging out deep holes in the process. When the mud-flat feeding grounds are laid nearly bare at low tide, the catfish congregate in these holes waiting for the water to return. They took a big catch of Gaff-Topsails, and with it the first definite information about what happens to the eggs.

Between two and three hundred eggs were obtained, all from the mouths of males. To make quite sure, the fishermen stood in the net in water and mud up to their waists, to keep the lead line on the bottom, and as the net came in, each fish was grasped just back of the head and in front of the great spine, to keep the mouth shut and to prevent the eggs from escaping. More eggs were taken during the same summer, but it takes a lot of collecting to get a complete series of embryos.

Then we come to the fateful experiences of most field naturalists trying to complete a project—Nature fails to co-op-

The Plumose anemone holds fast to a rock and spreads its flowerlike
head of tentacles as a trap to catch small swimming sea animals.

(*Above*) A Plumose anemone spawning its eggs. A wave of contraction travels up the column and the eggs pour out like dust in the water.

(*Below*) Plumose anemones also propagate by cuttings. The base of a contacted anemone withdraws, leaving a ring of small pieces, each growing into a new anemone.

Starfishes hunting on sponges. A brittle-star feeling within sponge cavities (*above*), and a common starfish and a smooth starfish crawling on sponge surface (*below*). The sponges are Crumb-of-bread sponges, and each crater is a water outlet.

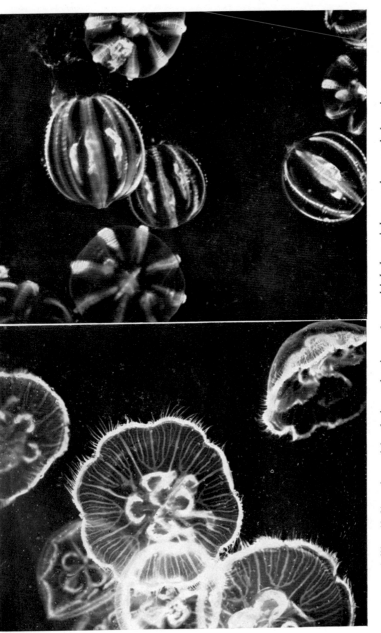

Moon-jellies (*left*) swim with their pulsating edge, which has eight notches each bearing an organ for balance. The reproductive glands are in the shape of four horseshoes. Comb-jellies (sea gooseberries) (*right*) swim by means of eight rows of beating combs, and glide like zeppelins.

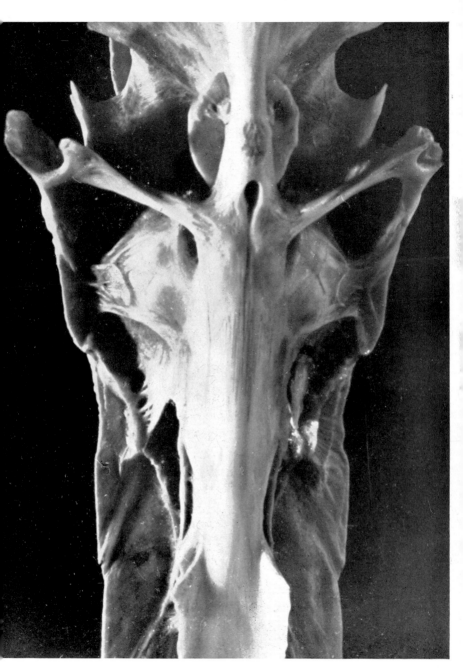

The Crucifix fish. The underside of the skull showing the crucifix, the figure outstretched on the cross, complete with halo.

(*Above*)
The Horseshoe crab is an antique unchanged in two hundred million
years. It has to dig its long spine into the ground to turn itself over.

(*Below*)
The Fiddler crab has a giant fiddle claw and a small bow claw. If it
loses its big claw, the small claw grows large.

A Hermit crab occupying the empty shell of a moon snail. Its tender and vulnerable tail is tucked safely out of sight, its pair of stalked eyes peer nervously out of the shelter, and only the heavily armored claws and legs are fully exposed.

(*Above*) A horde of starfish raiding a bed of mussels, with several whelks joining in the feast.

(*Below*) Squid in flashing colors swim backwards by jet-propulsion from the funnel under the neck.

A cluster of Hydroids, all grown from a single egg, and each in its
turn producing eggs like a bunch of grapes fastened below the head
and tentacles.

(*Above*) Brittle-star, showing central mouth and the patterns of five.

(*Below*) Sand Dollars. One upsidedown showing its central mouth and five rays, and one denuded shell.

Queen Trigger fish glides between staghorn coral above and brain coral below. The strong teeth serve to scrape seaweed off the rocks. A flip of the tail and the fish is out of sight behind a coral. (*Courtesy American Museum of Natural History*)

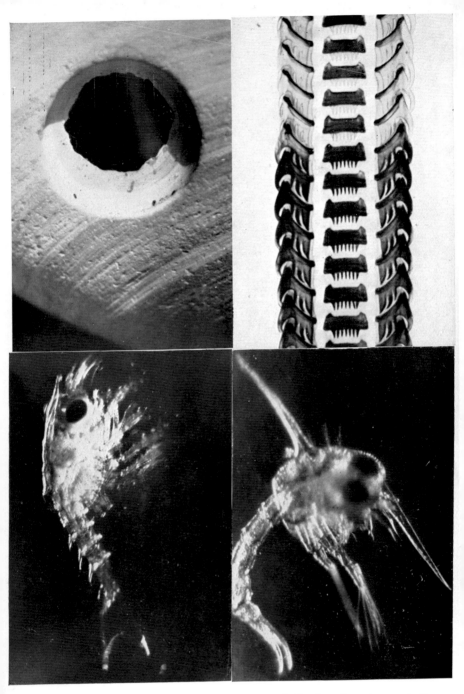

(*Above left*) Hole drilled and etched in the shell of a clam by a whelk.
(*Above right*) Part of rasping tooth-ribbon from the mouth of a whelk.
(*Below left*) Young lobster larva at quarter-inch free-swimming stage.
(*Below right*) Free-swimming Zoea larva of the shore crab, one tenth of
an inch, just hatched from egg.

A stalk-eyed Octopus swimming out of its lair in a dark corner of a coral grotto. Two long arms of another octopus hang down as their owner prepares to follow suit. (*Courtesy American Museum of Natural History*)

A fish-eye view of a Sea Raven. The mouth opens like a bear-trap, water rushes into the cavernous interior, taking in any hapless small fish with it. The two knobs above the mouth are the eyes which swing like turrets as they watch for prey.

Young Cormorants (*left*) in black down-feathers wait in their nest on the edge of a sea cliff. A young Seal pup (*right*), recently weaned, on deck of the fish-hatchery boat.

Cormorants nest in dead trees on the islands when trees can be found, otherwise on the ledges. These are young cormorants not yet able to leave their nests except by falling out.

erate! And for summer after summer, for the succeeding four years, heavy rains freshened the river and sent the catfish out to sea, or unseasonable frost upset the breeding dates and missing stages in the embryo series were missed. Even in apparently fine weather few fish and no eggs were taken, though a 1,200-foot seine drifted over a mile of the river.

The difficulties of the search and the tenacity of the searcher, whether or not he kept on "for Science" or for the same reason that a mountain-climber refuses to quit, are wonder enough. What should make any man stand aghast with apprehension is one of the investigation's findings—the ordeal of paternal fidelity that every male sea-cat must go through each summer. For two long months a male catfish less than two feet long may have to carry as many as fifty to sixty marble-sized eggs, four-fifths of an inch across, in its mouth. During all this time the male eats nothing, but keeps a strong stream of freshening water pouring through his mouth, across the eggs and out through the gills. Even when the eggs hatch into two-inch fish, they remain at home, skating across the floor of Father's mouth, weighted down by their large yolk sacs. Only when the yolk is gone and the babies are as long as four inches are they permitted to leave. The only thing I can think of that might be worse than keeping a bag of marbles in the mouth for a month or so, is having to refrain for weeks from spitting out several dozen healthy and vigorous fingerlings.

Gudger suggests the habit came about in this way—catfish which live in fresh water, their original home, scoop a sort of nest in the bottom gravel and deposit the eggs in it. The male stands guard and every once in a while takes the eggs into his mouth and spits them out again, to clean them of mud and debris. Even moderately large eggs are in constant danger of suffocation unless a good stream of water flows over them. It is not surprising therefore that when the lake and river catfish descended to the estuaries and the sea, it became necessary to pay still more attention to ensure the survival and development of the eggs. Large eggs spawned on shelly or sandy bottoms would be quickly eaten by the voracious blue crabs, and no catfish however determined could keep vicious, hungry crabs at bay for weeks on end. Nor could the eggs be laid on the muddy bottoms where the breeding fish are usually caught. Their weight would cause them to sink into the mud to be smothered. No, the problem had to be met in some such way as it actually has, or else the fish would have to travel upstream to a place of relative safety, and this is less likely than it seems, for it is no easy matter for a fish to switch from salt to fresh water and back again.

So the Gaff-Topsails stick to their murky salt water mud flats and do the best they can to raise a decent family. And after all, if the female can produce as magnificent fish eggs as these, the least the male can do is to take care of them the only way he can. These are the largest fish eggs in the world, and the female is entitled to do the loving and leaving, and abandon them to Father—their living perambulator.

CHAPTER TEN

SEA FOOD

IN FLORIDA it is fish, ornamental or sporting, but not so much to eat. In Maine it's lobsters, and plenty to eat. In Massachusetts it used to be clams, but that congested state long ago ate itself prodigally out of house and home and now imports sea stuff for native and visitor alike. But from there down to Hatteras the home-grown menu is blue crab and oyster, and here are the waters of the sea farmers.

The important thing about sea farming is not that it might be improved, which it might and must, but that it exists at all. Even in the sea it is possible to exploit and exhaust a stock beyond the "point of no return," and the oyster industry along our Atlantic coast, which began with the wasteful, free-for-all pillaging of extensive natural beds in Chesapeake Bay and Long Island Sound, has slowly come around to regulations and an approach to the oyster-farming methods so successful in France.

No cultivator needs to know more about his crop than the oyster farmer—about the finished article and its flavor, the seeding and growing, the control of pests and influence of climate—and no farming job is harder, for the soil and climate are both water.

What is an oyster? Take any good-sized freshly opened one

and examine it with care and you may soon try to forget it is edible. It is a bivalve certainly, but with an awful lot of shell for the amount of mollusk inside and a predilection to get stuck like few other bivalves to the spot they first sit upon. It is a complex creature and superbly made. The enveloping web within the shell is the mantle which manufactures the limy shell and the occasional pearl. In the middle is the large slab of muscle that holds the shells together. The heart lies on the hinge side of the muscle and, believe it or not, the intestine passes right through its center. Lift the mantle and you can see the gill curtains, four in all, with the foot lying between them. There is nothing you can call a head, no means of moving, and yet it is one of the most efficient animals in the sea. The secret lies in the nature of the gill curtains.

The gills of oysters, clams, mussels and scallops all have the same essential structure. They have a fine grid pattern of ridges and grooves covered with minute protoplasmic hairs. These hairs beat rhythmically and their action draws in a current of water from the surrounding sea. With the water come all manner of minute plant and animal organisms that can be used as food. These flow with the water over the gills and are sorted out by the grid, the smallest going to the mouth for dinner, the too-large passing on to leave with the outgoing water. In short, the oyster and its kind act as water filters, purifying the water not so much to clean it, but just the reverse— to extract the impurities on which they live. To do this the oyster needn't move at all as long as its original choice of seat was good and stays good. Why this is the crux of the situation will become apparent.

Whatever the original reason for not eating oysters during

the months that have no "R" in them, the rule is fine for the oyster race. Oysters distend with spawn during the spring and in Virginia waters they shed their eggs from June till October. The number of eggs laid in one season by a large Virginia oyster may number nearly half a billion. Multiply that by the number of female oysters in Chesapeake and though the resulting potential oysters annually set free is an astronomical figure, its main significance is that it emphasizes the overwhelming improbability that any one oyster egg will ever grow into an adult oyster. The miracle is that any do.

Eggs and milt are shed freely into the water. After about thirty hours, depending on the temperature, a young oyster called the "straight-line larva" develops, no more than one five-hundredth of an inch across. The two oyster shells have already started to grow. After two or three more days the two shells not only change their shape but become different from one another. This distinction alone makes it possible to tell an oyster larva from any of the numerous young clams and mussels swimming about nearby. Then it drives through the water like a microscopic submerged hydroplane, its propeller a girdle of long regularly beating protoplasmic hairs, called a velum, that both pulls the larva along and at the same time draws food particles toward the mouth. Finally, after eight to ten days of this, it settles down on the sea floor.

Once on the bottom the motile oyster still glides along, its slender little foot probing for a suitable place for final attachment. This is the oyster spat. If the spat has found a good spot, a tiny though recognizable oyster can be seen after a couple of days, not much larger than a pin head, but with the characteristic oyster shape. And while it is small, it is already about ten times as long as the free swimming larva.

What, then, makes one spot better than another? The answer is short and simple—just clean oyster shells. Dead and empty oyster shells are usually common in any natural oyster bed, and young oysters continually grow on top of the remains of previous generations. If the water is too warm, however, as in Chesapeake Bay, many other kinds of marine growth, animal and plant, also settle on the oyster shell to make a sort of forest in miniature. The shells are then fouled and there are comparatively few spots free for spat to make its home. So an oyster "strike" can be a poor one even if dead shells are abundant. This is where farming begins.

As in dirt-farming, when you want to plant a crop you first prepare the ground. In the case of oysters this can be done in several ways. In public grounds, a "culch" is maintained, that is, a perpetual bed of dead oyster shells kept in good condition, so that the larvae can strike and good spat form. This is done by dumping old shells on to the beds, and in the Chesapeake some three million bushels of them have been planted during fifteen years. This obviously was not enough and so in Virginia there is the Cull Law, providing that all dead shells without spat must be returned to the beds, as well as all oysters less than three inches long. Only three-year-olds, between three and four inches long, can be taken. In this way an animal crop of only mature oysters is gathered. Larger oysters can be kept, of course, but except in newly discovered beds they have little chance of growing much beyond the legal limits.

Private oyster grounds are often cultivated in another way. Seed oysters collected from natural seeding grounds are planted and allowed to grow for three or four years. Then the crop is gathered and the ground cleared and replanted, as in good lumbering.

We can call this farming, for it is farming in contrast to the mining practice employed in the fisheries industry as a whole, where claim after claim is being short-sightedly worked out. But it is a primitive kind of farming, like the pioneer sod-breaking of the prairies, compared with the oyster-farming now in practice along the west coast of France.

The story goes back, as it always does, to a crisis and the inspired imagination of an individual. When the oyster stock first became ominously low, in the middle of the last century, the government called in Professor Coste of the College of France to investigate. The first experiments consisted merely of efforts to restock old beds with imported oysters. They were highly successful. This was the new idea. The old idea, long forgotten, was the ancient practice of the Romans of collecting spat on bundles of twigs. Put new ideas and old together and like wine, something usually happens. In this case it happened to Coste, for he foresaw that by collecting spat wholesale it would be possible to cultivate oysters wholesale. Everything was set to go. When Emperor Napoleon III joined up and established two Imperial Oyster Parks in the shallow bay of Arcachon, what could the oyster do but respond?

It took a long time to work out the methods now in use in what has become a great French industry, and the procedures go far beyond rough farming and can be compared only with modern horticulture. Spat are now collected on half-round roofing tiles that have been covered with a mixture of lime and sand. The mortar, together with the tiny oysters, is flaked off and then, like real seeds too delicate to be set out at once, are placed in "ambulances" or wooden frames resting on short legs, with wire mesh above and below. In this way the minute oysters are protected from most of their enemies and from the smothering mud. Here they grow until they reach the size of fine seed oysters, large enough to be placed in the open sea. Then they are set out in oyster parks between the tides, each park surrounded by a palisade of twigs, and left there to grow for two years until almost two inches across. The final step is more akin to cattle ranching than growing tomatoes, which is logical, for after all, oysters are animals even though they seem to live a vegetable existence. They are sent to fattening farms for almost a year until ready for market. And four to five hundred million oysters are exported every year to the connoisseurs of Europe.

Oysters have more to worry about than we have, and less to worry with. Their troubles begin even before the spat is formed. Sometimes, just before a strike, the water over the beds may be milky with larva oysters about to settle, and Chesapeake oyster farmers watch with their fingers crossed. A sudden drop in temperature could kill the larvae in a few hours, or an offshore wind might suddenly drive the surface water and larvae out to sea, and no spat will form on the waiting beds. Even when the beds are flourishing and the oysters nearly ready for market, an excessive run-off from the Susquehanna watershed can turn the upper reaches of the Chesapeake so brackish that the oysters in these parts are killed. It has happened too many times.

Quite apart from the elements, the oyster farmers have as

much trouble with pests as the cornbelt farmers have with the corn-borer. Only instead of an insect, which cannot live in the sea, it is a sea snail. A horde of invading starfishes may do more damage to an oyster bed in a short time, but this snail, the oyster drill, lives among the oysters and takes its time and toll. The toll is a high one, probably close to fifty per cent of the maturing Virginia oysters.

The drill is a little whelk about one inch long that feeds upon bivalves generally and the oyster when it can. Water has to be more than half brackish before drills are discouraged and oysters themselves dislike water much fresher than that. Oyster shell is exceedingly thick, but this avails nothing when time is of no account. A drill settles down on its chosen oyster and starts to work. Little by little, at the rate of one fiftieth of an inch every twenty-four hours, a small hole is drilled through the shell, as a rule over the region where the muscle is attached. The oyster dies soon after the hole is made—it seems that a poison is injected through the hole which paralyzes and kills the animal within. One oyster ought to last a small drill a long time, but while the drill feeds through its private pipeline, the oyster shells open and crabs and other scavengers join the feast. So after a while the drill moves on to begin on a new oyster, and in a season one drill may kill from thirty to two hundred oysters, depending on their size. Remember, too, that drills kill and eat oysters from the time each is born, so to speak.

Drills are either male or female, something we might take for granted but should not, and when the breeding season arrives the females creep higher on the bed and lay vase-like capsules of eggs on the oyster shells themselves. In place of the enormous number of microscopic eggs of the oyster, each drill capsule contains about ten eggs of a relatively large size. In a little more than a month they hatch out as tiny drills just about the size of week-old spat. The young drills hatch on the oyster shells, never swim about, and start to feed at once on baby oysters not much larger than themselves. They take their toll not merely of the large oysters, but of oysters on every step of the way. And once again we find a common trouble of all farmers. When seed stock is transplanted from one place to another the pests usually go along with it, and like potatoes and potato beetles, oyster and oyster drill eggs have been moved around together wherever oysters have been planted, even from the Chesapeake to San Francisco Bay.

I doubt if oyster swallowers ever think about the oyster's sex. It probably is definitely male or female at the time, though the queer part of an oyster's sex life is its turnabout. Virginia oysters mature first as males and begin to discharge spermatozoa when about five months old. By the time the sperm is all shed, the sex glands are already beginning to change to female and at six months are busy producing eggs. But the California oyster, like the Chamber of Commerce, doesn't know when to stop. Having been a male, having changed to female and shed its first batch of eggs, it swings back to being a male, and from then on, every few months for the rest of its life, it changes from one sex to the other. And why not? The oyster's life, what with whelks and men, can be, as one non-zoologist has put it, an awful bore.

How well oysters and crabs mix gastronomically is an argument beyond our scope, but living blue-points and living blue crabs occupy much the same territory and share, moreover, blueness of another kind. Each has blue blood, a very pale blue to be sure, but blue nevertheless and not pink or red. The color comes from copper in the blood, and takes the place of the iron in the red haemoglobin of men, fish and angle-worms.

Two hundred million blue crabs is a lot of crab, yet that is the annual crop of the Chesapeake waters alone. Not any kind of blue crab mind you, but merely the softshells that are marketed.

In one sense of the word, blue crabs are farmed or at least cultivated, though only through collective activity and not by any small group of individuals. For in this case the crop doesn't stay put. The whole of Chesapeake Bay is needed for the seeding, growing and reaping of a single crop, and as much space is needed in other districts.

In the jargon of the industry there are three kinds of crabs— hardshell, softshell and peelers, not to mention sponge crabs, buckrams and Jimmies. And in the language of the Government biologists there are also such things as a zoea, a megalops, and instars.

A sponge crab is a female crab carrying a spongy mass of eggs, about two million of them, stuck to appendages beneath the tail. Crabs do have tails, tucked under and held close to the lower side of the body. Eggs are squeezed through the ducts into the waiting cradle formed by the tail, coupling having taken place long before.

After two or three weeks each pinhead-sized egg hatches into a zoea and swims away toward the sea surface. Why it was first called a zoea I am not sure, except that there was no reason why anyone should have recognized it as a young crab. Apart from its small size and marine nature it could readily pass for someone from Mars, with its helmet-shaped, spike-topped body, long tail, enormous eyes, long pointed nose and six hand-bearing arms. Size and what you are used to seeing makes all the difference. An elephant the size of a rabbit would look cute, but a beetle of the same size would give you a fit.

A zoea starts life when one twenty-fifth of an inch long, and if half the crabs which are caught are female, then those taken in one year from Chesapeake Bay would have produced about two hundred billion zoeas the following year. Obviously a zoea does not stay a zoea, though it has the same difficulty in growing that an adult crab has. Its skin is not elastic and must be cast before growth can take place. This the zoea does five times, by which time it has grown a bit and discards its baby clothes. Then the megalops takes its place, and this form actually does look like a small crab, apart from the tail which still sticks out. All this takes about a month, and at the next skin cast, or molt, a young crab about one tenth of an inch wide sinks to the sea floor and hopes for the best. Already most of those that hatched from the eggs will have been swallowed by fish or jellyfish.

At first the young crab molts every few days, and then less and less frequently until the molts are several weeks apart. In a year they are large enough to be marketed, from three to four inches across. Then, if they are not caught or killed, the cycle starts over again. Female crabs that have mated move from the brackish upper reaches of the Chesapeake down to the saltier water near the mouth of the Bay. Sponge-formation or egg-laying begins in May and lasts through the summer. A new crop of zoeas, megalops and young crabs appear and eventually settle. Those still within the Bay grow and migrate toward the brackish waters of the rivers and upper Bay. They hibernate during the cold winter temperatures and finally become peelers the following summer. As such they can be legally caught. Mating occurs in the head tide waters and then the females migrate seaward as before, to spawn the following spring in the waters between the Virginia Capes. So that altogether there is a two-year cycle, the crabs reaching sexual maturity at the end of one year and spawning when two years old.

This cycle brings us to the first steps in the maintenance of a good crab population. A Sanctuary for breeding crabs is set aside in Virginia waters between Hampton Roads and the Atlantic Ocean. Maryland prohibits the taking of crabs in November, thus favoring the migration southward of the mated crabs.

The difficulty in conserving supplies is less a matter of regulating fishing methods and periods than it is the problem of marketing crabs when the shell is soft. That is, when the crab has just cast its old hard shell. Naturally, crabs are caught at all stages. The so-called peeler crabs, which should molt within a few days of being caught, are placed in wooden floats. Just before molting, a red line appears round the edge of the back fins, and at this time a soft shell already exists under the hard shell. In the course of half an hour the old shell is thrown off. If the line is white or green, the crabs are not only too far from the next molting period, but they will also eat soft-shell crabs. Consequently the floats are continually "fished" by experienced men for the soft-shell crabs that have recently shed, and "green" crabs, "white line" crabs, and "red line" crabs are sorted and placed in separate floats, a tiresome procedure that takes a lot of time. But it is in the floats that the greatest loss of crabs takes place. In some years, as much as fifty per cent of the crabs die in the floats, and it is the practice of keeping the green and white line crabs in there too long which is mainly responsible. Altogether it is a complicated matter—a challenge both to biologists and administrators to work out a detailed interstate crab-crop management.

CHAPTER ELEVEN

PILGRIM SHORE

THE New England evening was mellow as the late-summer sun sank across Cape Cod Bay. At Orleans on the Cape the sea cuts in from east and west and leaves no more than a mile of glacial sand between, for the Cape itself is no more than the sandy terminal dumping-ground, or "moraine," of a great glacier. Here, still farther north in our progress up the Atlantic coast, I was on vacation. But you never can tell, and while laboratories large and small are fine, I had with me all the equipment I ever need—a microscope, a thermometer and a watch, plus some glassware and drawing materials. And the Cape sands were as good a place as any to study the one-sided, ancient battle of Clam versus Snail, a contest more recently widened to Clam versus Snail plus Man.

The clam-draggers had come up the creek to unload, and hard-shelled quahogs were piled into waiting barrels. Through the still night the boats rested sand-borne while the sea ebbed away from them, then as the dawn came and the water with it, they were gone. As the sun climbed towards the zenith the sea ebbed again, almost to the horizon, and sands as flat as a race-track extended as far as you could see and only the tiny figures of distant clam-diggers following close behind the receding water's edge showed where the sea lay.

The temptation to follow it was too great, and my wife and I took our three youngsters across the wet sands, splashing ankle-deep through long stretches of shallow pools. Invisible sand-colored shrimps darted through the water across our naked feet, flicking the skin as they flipped their tails. Hermit crabs scuttled away, clearly with no idea of where to go, absurd mixtures of heroes and cowards, each with its soft rear-end tucked safely away inside an empty snail shell. Here and there a shell showed pink and fluffy under the rippling water, and when we looked closely we could see a carpet of tiny, waving hydroids, each like a minute sea anemone.

Here most hermits dragged around the shell of the lesser moon snail (called a shark's-eye shell) and we wondered where they had found them until we saw small humps of sand gliding slowly along the shallows. Then it became a game to see who could find the snail with the biggest foot, and the smallest child won. Size for size, I think this snail has the largest crawling foot of its kind in the world, and it is always amazing to watch this mollusk pull back the enormous mass of muscle into its shell, and close the door with the horny opercular shield fastened to the back of the foot. It always manages, though toward the end the effort is obvious. In the sand, this foot slides out and glides below the surface like a flatiron, the round shell curved like a turret to protect the vulnerable organs inside. Even the sensitive head is protected, for as the snail drives blindly through the sand it pulls a protective hood of tissue over what might charitably be called its face.

The moon snails were common. What were their means of support? We felt the clam-diggers had some connection—true enough, for snails and diggers both had the same idea—to get clams. And as long as a moon snail in a clam-flat keeps moving, it will sooner or later bump into a clam, and an unlucky one at that.

These lesser moon snails were feeding on the long-neck clams, the kind you feed on when they're served steaming on a platter in a fish-house. Even within the world of clam and moon snail there is a fine adjustment—the lesser moon snail lives inshore, above the level of low tide, and dines on the long-neck. The greater moon snail, a whopper with a shell sometimes as big as a tennis ball and a foot with a ten-inch span, picks up where its smaller relative leaves off, from low-water mark down to deeper water. While it would undoubtedly welcome for lunch a long-neck with its shells that cannot fully close, it has to go after tougher kinds, the hard, vise-tight quahogs and the hen or surf clams.

In their own watery way the snail and clam repeat the drama of the mountain lion and the deer. The clam, like the deer, feeds directly upon the green stuff which lives on water, salts and sunlight. The snail, like the mountain lion, feeds on the clam. Only in place of grass or foliage, the sea plants are microscopic. Any clam is, in fact, essentially a filter system and can even be employed to purify an aquarium—it continually draws a current of water in through its funnel and sifts out the minute, single-celled plants contained in the stream. It is a delicate and beautifully intricate mechanism, but it needs neither brain nor eyes, nor much activity, and so remains buried in the sand or mud, with its funnel just reaching to the surface where clean water can be inhaled. It can do nothing but stay put, feed, grow, and take a chance on being eaten. Moon snails will eat nothing but the meat of living clams, and

E

like all predators their numbers are closely related to the size of the population upon which they feed.

A long-neck clam offers little trouble to any moon snail, but a tightly closed quahog is more than a man can open without a knife. Moon snails have their own special equipment for the job and they use it effectively. The attack, when it comes, is as formidable, overwhelming and in effect as deadly as the spring and landing crash of the lion. The huge foot, three times as long as its shell, ripples lightly around the shell of the victim, glides over it and enfolds it firmly. Then down comes the hood, the long tubular proboscis is put in place, and the drill starts to act. It is an instrument that all snails and whelks possess, a ribbon of closely set teeth known as a radula. It works like a rasp and can be used to scrape vegetation of a rock, or in the case of our mole-like, meat-eating moon snail to scrape away the horny layer covering the thick shell of the quahog. The neat, round hole that you find near the hinge of most of the empty clam shells along an open beach is made after the radula has done its preliminary scraping. It is made by the action of the boring gland. The radula, like a rasp, cannot be rotated as a drill and the round deep hole is actually etched out of the living shell by sulphuric acid produced by the circular boring gland lying just beneath the tip of the proboscis. Once the hole is made, the radula comes into its own again, scraping the soft inner tissues of the victim into fragments and passing them back to the gizzard. And here, surprisingly, to complete what has been already a pretty good effort at mastication, stomach teeth take over and grind the food up in the midst of the digestive juices. At times a man gnashes his teeth in anger, and maybe we should be thankful our teeth are where they are, for anything more disconcerting than powerful molars suddenly clenching and grinding in the pit of the stomach I cannot imagine.

Most marine whelks and snails possess this combination of rasp, acid-borer and gastric mill. What they use it on depends mainly on chance encounter and the size of the victim.

Moon snails play havoc with both the quahog little-necks and the soft-shell long necks. Neither of these can get away and have to take what comes. Soft-shell clams are not drilled. It's not necessary—they cannot close their shells sufficiently to keep out the moon snail proboscis. If you ask for "sand-gapers" in an English fishmarket, this is the clam you will get. The Indian name for it was "maninose," converted to "nanny-nose" by the Colonists, a name still heard along the coast. It was from the Indians the Pilgrims first learned of its value, and John Winthrop lists it, in 1634, among the animals at Plymouth as "Clams—white. Their broth is most excellent in all intermitting fevers, consumption, etc. These clams feed only on sand."

Yet even with man left out of the picture, the moon snails are not the poor clam's only enemies. The large knobbed and channeled whelks that live along the whole sandy Atlantic coastline flourish on a diet of clams. These are the whelks with a long, hollow channel, almost a funnel, of shell extending in front. This contains the respiratory siphons and makes it possible for the owner to burrow away in the sand in search of prey while sending its siphons above the surface, like the periscope of a submarine, to get clean water to breathe. The big whelks may not be quite so deadly as the moon snails, but they are as large and they are faster. Probably because of this they are able to include the surf clam among their choicest meals. Largest bivalve on the Atlantic coast, the surf clam lives beneath the surf-line where it travels just below the sand surface, and has such a powerful foot that it can actually leap and so escape its enemies, whether they be giant whelks or starfishes. Not all of them escape, as drilled shells show, though at least when the enemy is the moon snail the victim is the more agile.

If the clam had any sense he'd find it profitable to stir up an argument between the snails and whelks, for a moon snail can lick a whelk, and size for size, the moon snail is the better fighter. Its great foot can smother a whelk. If the snail lays hold of a whelk, the whelk withdraws into its shell and closes the door tightly with its operculum. But it still has to breathe, and once in a while the door must open to exchange stale water for fresh. Otherwise it smothers, and if a moon snail succeeds in wrapping its foot around the whelk, it does smother. A moon snail will do the same to its own kind if given a chance, and will either smother it or drill it. Anything for a good meal.

Farther south, along the coast of Florida, a similar game is played, with variations. The big whelks are in on it, for they lay their long, peculiar egg-ribbons along the whole length of the Atlantic coast, each ribbon like a yard-long string of thick coins. And even in Florida the whelks have to contend with the avid appetite of the moon snails. Two additional players take a hand. One of these is no larger than the whelks, yet it seems to have a tactic that the others lack. It is a whelk or snail, whichever you like, called the crowned melangena, and it acts as though it may actually possess intelligence, although intelligence would be an amazing thing to find in the tiny brain of a sea snail. Melangenas will eat what they can get, with a preference for oysters, and, failing oysters, clams or whelks. Now, it is a common sight to see maybe a dozen melangenas sitting closely around a tired oyster or in a tight circle around a whelk. As the oyster shells gape or as the whelk lifts its operculum to breathe, in go the snouts like long, tough, black shoestrings. The victim clamps down on them, but before long needs to breathe again, and the snouts push in farther. In the end they get in far enough for the rasping radulas to get to work, and all is over.

At other times they may be seen circling in back of a resting scallop in order to sneak up behind and approach within pouncing distance before the agile scallop becomes aware of danger. For a scallop can see and is blind only towards the rear. Yet even Melangena is not immune to attack. The Great Band Snail roams the reefs and banks, the largest seasnail in the world, often two feet long. When it encounters a melangena unwilling to give up its meal, it simply walks over it and around it and smothers it to death, and so gets two meals in one.

Only a little less formidable is the Giant Conch, a heavy-weight running as high as five pounds and not wanting in power. It is a carrion-eater, and though perfectly able to handle live clams, most of its efforts go into the hunting of dead fish and other things along the reefs. But it is pugnacious and active and when stranded by the tide makes good use of its claw-like operculum. The extended hook is stuck into the wet sand and over rolls the shell. The next stroke flings it in another direction, and at last, after hurtling violently one way and then another, it plunks into the water. There is little doubt that where the Florida heat enervates a man it activates a mollusk or a crab.

Everything is slower in the colder waters of New England, and neither snails nor crabs, large or small, move any faster than seems proper. No one was ever startled by a moon snail, though many have sworn at it.

And so the struggle goes on. It is a natural one, and wherever there is a community of vegetarians in the sea or on land there is normally a group of carnivores preying upon it, and a balance is struck. On land man has stupidly upset the balance by killing off most of the beasts and birds of prey, so that the vegetarians flourish and we have plagues of ground rodents and grain-eating birds. We have no appetite for gophers, mice and starlings, but now we have to put up with them.

In the sea things are a little different, so far. The moon snails maintain themselves very nicely on the clam beds and there seems to be nothing wrong with that if we ignore the view of the luckless and brainless clam. Of course human beings like clams too, and they are a greedy race. Speaking more for myself than for most marine zoologists, one can get too familiar with details of the internal anatomy of creeping, crawling sea creatures ever to forget them. You cannot swallow an oyster and a mental blueprint of his anatomy at the same time. Together they stick in the throat, and it is the oyster that comes up. When visitors come to our home in Maine we show them the nicest sea food restaurant in town. We may even throw a clam-bake for them. But we take hamburgers ourselves.

Glamorous-looking or not, though, sea food is nourishing

and we, collectively this time, want all the clams we can get, including those the moon snails eat. The difficulty is to discourage, or eliminate, the moon snails. Before the Pilgrims came the clams and moon snails were naturally both getting along fine, and when clams get scarce today we might look first to see who is catching most of them, and who might be polluting the waters.

But the moon snails do take a heavy toll, and the outcome of their gustatory efforts and ours is a great deal of time and funds spent finding out ways of killing off snails, discovering why clams disappear from old beds or don't grow properly, and establishing clams in new places. Recently some 300,000 seed quahogs—any quahog under three inches—were dropped by air into Casco Bay. From a height of twenty-five feet each bushel spreads out over forty square yards, and although it's a quick way of spreading clams, transplanting is neither new nor sure-fire. Giant Pacific Coast Geoducks, the huge long-necked clams that set a weight record of sixteen pounds, were flown from Puget Sound only to have them scorn the water and mud of Maine and promptly die.

When it comes to the native long-necks, once so abundant along the New England shore, the situation becomes serious. Commercial harvesting on Cape Cod and the rest of the Pilgrim State is practically a thing of the past, and Massachusetts now has to import annually nearly ten million dollars worth of soft-shell clams from places less devastated.

Moon snails are partly responsible, so is eel grass and so is the clam-digger. As clams get scarcer, clam-diggers get more efficient. One of their latest mechanical aids is a wristwatch, set to local tide readings, that not only shows its wearer the exact rate of ebb and flow on two small dials but advances daily, one-half to one-and-a-half hours later than the preceding day, just as the tide does.

The clam-digger's watch literally gazes at the moon, and so do the moon snails, which spawn not according to whim but according to moon and tide. More than likely if you have walked along the Atlantic beaches you have come across their egg masses. They look as much as anything like a clergyman's collar, and collars they are called. The eggs are extruded from the body of the snail as a continuous gelatinous sheet in which the eggs are imbedded. As fast as the sheet emerges it is covered with sand, cemented together with a mucous secretion. The expanding mass slides round the snail, taking its shape from the shape of the foot and shell of the snail as it goes. Once formed, the collars rest on the sand or mud with the wide edge well lodged, and it takes a lot of wave action to upset them. Eventually the jelly softens, the collar disintegrates and young moon snails are set free.

Here we come to one of those superb little cases of adjustment between an animal and the place in which it lives. The lesser moon snail lives on the flats between the tides, the greater moon snail below the low water. The small snail lays a small collar, the large snail a large one. But quite apart from size the collars are less alike than they seem. The large collars may be very large or not so large, depending on the age and size of the snail, and if you examine one with a hand lens you can see that there are a large number of small compartments each containing microscopic eggs, half a dozen in each compartment in a small collar, and as many as fifty in a larger. When they hatch out the tiny larvae swim away in the currents and only the favored few survive to settle on the sea floor. Between the tides they would have little chance indeed.

Now, you might expect the small moon snails to produce the same kind of eggs, only fewer of them. If they did, the chances are that they would be too few in number to ensure the survival of the race, considering the choice of habitat. What we do find is that the number of compartments, even for a small-sized collar, is greatly reduced, and each one contains a single large egg. Thus in place of numerous microscopic seed scattered to all points of the compass, a comparatively few but relatively large young moon snails emerge from the collar to start crawling and feeding alongside the grown-ups. And what they need for food is there from the start. The smallest snails feed at once upon the smallest clams, the seed of one on the seed of the other, and so on up the scale of growth until maturity feeds on maturity and then casts around for bigger and better prey, maybe their own brothers and sisters I was about to say, but I cannot because each snail is both sister and brother at once, both male and female in each individual. At least there are no idle males to eat more than their worth or waste their time to no good purpose.

CHAPTER TWELVE

MAINE LOBSTER

"AND towards night we drew with a small net of twenty fathoms very nigh the shore; we got about thirty very good and great lobsters . . . which I omit not to report, because it sheweth how great a profit the fishing would be. . . ." So wrote Waymouth in the Journal of his voyage to the Coast of Maine, in 1605.

Three-and-one-half centuries later the Maine lobster fishing is still good, though the days of the "great" lobster are gone. Intensive fishing and close regulation, in effect for many years now, have prevented all but a very few lobsters from reaching any great age or size. I have risen before dawn to go out with the lobstermen, and it is seldom that they get a catch with more than half the lobsters in it of legal size or over. But big lobsters or small, state regulations and canny, downeast shrewdness have kept the Maine lobster industry in a robust condition where neighboring Massachusetts caught and ate up their local supply long before the Civil War. Non-residents of Maine were prohibited from catching lobsters as early as 1823, and though I can sit on a rock at the end of Lobster Cove near Boothbay Harbor and call it our own, I cannot set a trap and I cannot touch the lobster buoy within reach of my hand—we are summer residents.

Lobsters took a beating when canning them was in vogue. There was a nine-inch law that tried to save them, but nine inches barely permits a lobster to grow big enough to produce eggs, and the industry, as usual, was trying its best to commit suicide by carefully avoiding the slightest pretexts at conservation. The ten-and-a-half inch law passed in 1895 produced a revolution. Lobster-canning folded up overnight, lobsters spawned in increasing numbers and the fresh-lobster industry began a boom that today has 6,500 lobstermen catching and selling between fifteen and twenty million lobsters a year. The State began an annual purchase of from twenty to forty thousand seeders, or egg-bearing lobsters, for planting and several thousand more for hatcheries, and protection is given not only to young adults but to any lobster smart enough to stay out of a trap for several more years. The reason is simple—a lobster in its first egg-laying season carries 9,000 to 10,000 eggs; if it lives long enough it may carry as many as 100,000 at a time. So it pays to let the valuable older ladies live.

Age and growth do queer things to a lobster. Claws and body grow at different rates, and in a very small lobster the claws are hardly worth the picking. The larger the lobster grows, the larger grow the claws, not at the same rate but faster, until at last in those giants you sometimes see in public aquaria but never in a fish market, the unbelievable happens and the tail wags the dog. The giant of them all was a lobster that weighed thirty-five pounds, as heavy as a child in a nursery school, with claws alone weighing more than two-thirds of the total. It is a wonder that a lobster can feed itself with such cumbersome weights to lift, though when an animal lives in water, its weight is only the difference between its weight in air and the weight of the same volume of water. All the same, such a lobster is quite a sight, a lumbering tank that moves slowly and no more than it must, which is not much, for neither the clams or mussels it eats can run away. It bothers few other animals and there is not much in the sea that can make a dent in a lobster.

Freshly caught lobsters do not always go straight to market. Most lobstermen keep a small "live-car" afloat near their moorings, and the tidal pounds up and down the Maine coast can keep about five million lobsters more or less happily waiting for the right price. They are fed mussels, though the lobsters do what they can on their own to supplement the monotony, and dig, shuck and eat the clams generally to be found in the muddy bottoms of the pounds. The idea of impounding lobsters behind a barrier that lets the greater part of the tide in and out but holds the lobsters behind bars is by no means new. The French took such matters seriously long before the rest of us. I remember a visit to a famous marine biological research laboratory at Roscoff on the north coast of Brittany where ancient lobster pounds were operated by the town and hundreds of thousands of lobsters awaited the Paris market.

On this continent you get the American lobster, with its great claws, along the middle and east Atlantic coast, the Spiny lobster or crawfish in the South and along the Pacific, with no claws to speak of and with over-long feelers. In Europe you can add a third, the little Norway lobster, and in that little French town I had them all, one after the other or all at once, the Norwegians piled high like shrimps, the crawfish as stew, and the other as straight lobster. But it was the heavy, brittle shell of a Norway lobster that cut my finger to the bone, and I know those lobsters by sight, smell and taste, and by touch and pain.

The table of course is no place to study what food was like when it was alive. But if you are tough-minded or can get a lobster on to your lap before it gets into the pot, it is worthwhile looking at it for what it is, a marvelously fitted piece of machinery designed for living.

We are inclined to take our commonplaces for granted. A lobster has a front and a back end, eyes, a heart, and some kind of a brain. "Naturally," you might say, yet it's not "naturally." A starfish or a jellyfish has none of these. The shape of a lobster means that it goes forwards or backwards, but not sideways like a crab. Feelers and eyes at the front end mean that it is built primarily for going forwards. But the shape of the body (streamlined towards the tail), the powerful muscles of the tail itself, and the broad fan at the end of the tail, are all directed toward fast, sudden movement to the *rear* as a means of escape.

The place for the pilot of a ship or a plane is on the bridge or in the cockpit. A lobster or a fish has its navigating instruments at the front end too, with the central brain control immediately behind. Everything is in pairs, for direction finding and for operational control. Fish and lobsters are not relatives, at least no more than you and a flea are, and yet each has eyes, each of its own kind, for supplying both light, direction and images. Each can touch, smell and taste, an intimate contact with the watery world without. And both are aware of gravity, the fish with parts of its ears and the lobster with an organ at the base of each long antenna.

The information that a lobster has a sense of gravity is more than guesswork and comes from a trick somebody once played upon one. . . .

Most animals that swim, run or fly have what seem to be gravity organs, all very much alike, small sacs of sensory tissue enclosing little heavy stones that shift about as the animals move. Lobsters and their tribe have a pair of sacs that appear to serve the same purpose. But they are unusual. They are not closed sacs but are depressions of the outer surface of the body which retain the openings to the outside, while in place of stones secreted by the animal itself, the weights within the sacs are sand-grains placed there by the lobster. Yet appearances can always be deceptive and such organs need not necessarily be what they seem to be. Experimental proof was possible simply because a lobster had to shed its skin periodically, and the shedding includes more than you would think, not merely the shell or skin of the outer body, claws and legs, but the lining of the stomach and intestine, and the lining of these balancer sacs. Whenever this happens, the soft-shelled lobster has to insert a fresh supply of sand-grains to replace those lost with the old skin. Here was the trick, obvious enough when you read about it but a stroke of genius at the time. Iron filings were made available to the lobster in place of sand. It put some into its sacs without knowing the difference, and apart from inevitable rusting I imagine it would have gotten along perfectly well. But iron filings respond to a magnet whereas sand does not, and the pull of a magnet is like the pull of the earth. The magnet was held over the head of the lobster, the filings flew up toward it and pressed against the part of the sacs normally stimulated only when a lobster is upside-down. The lobster reacted according to information received and turned itself completely over. The response was correct. But the information received was false, and the lobster lay on its back, a lost and tragic crustacean.

This business of casting skins is complicated. Even the covering of the eyes is included, and sometimes an eye and eyestalk is lost in the process. How much it matters depends on how much is lost. If the eye alone is lost, a new one soon grows to take its place and normal vision is regained, quite a startling performance in itself. But if the whole thing is lost, eye and stalk together, something grows, but it is no longer an eye and looks like a small antenna.

Look for a moment (if it is still on your lap) at the lower side of the animal. There is one long series of paired appendages. They show what a centipede might have done with its hundred pairs of legs, but didn't. No one needs as many legs as that, and the lobster settled for five pairs, then found that four were plenty and used the first pair as enlarged claws for feeding. And since a knife and fork are better than two knives, one claw has become a crusher and the other a cutter. Even after the food has been cut up into small pieces, the lobster handles it in a most delicate way, using as many as six pairs of jaws or jaw accessories to get it into the narrow gullet. More than that, when the food does reach the stomach, the gastric mill with its teeth, rods, and muscles, grinds it up with the digestive juices.

So much for food. What about oxygen? Blue blood needs it as much as red, and gets it through the gills. These are cream-colored, feathery structures hidden from view beneath the armor at the sides of the body, and water is bailed through them continuously. These gills have an interest quite apart from their respiratory function. Each grows from the base of a leg, and each leg unit is a double feature, one branch for breathing and another for walking. It is as if your shoulder muscles operated not only your arms but a pair of wings you may be hoping to sprout one day. The image that comes first to my mind is of a one-man band I saw not long ago, with hands and forearms working an accordion and drum sticks fastened to the elbows beating a drum on the man's back.

Double-duty seems to be a lobster commonplace. The appendages beneath the tail have different things to do at different times. They are called swimmerets, which tells something about them, for when a lobster wants to move forward when its legs are off the sea floor, the swimmerets paddle in a regular rhythm and the animal actually swims. This is their main purpose, but another use has crept in. When it comes time to spawn, the eggs are fertilized with sperm stored from the year before in pockets behind the legs and then are glued to the swimmerets. And there they stay until they hatch, rocked gently in the water for the best part of a year. It seems a long time for such a small egg to develop, but for much of the time little actually goes on. There is a quick start during the first summer, then a slowing of development almost to a complete stop as the sea temperatures fall with the bitter cold of the North Atlantic winter. When spring warmth returns, if you can call it that, development speeds up to a quick finish and the young lobsters hatch in water already teeming with the microscopic life they need as food.

For many years the "berried" lobsters have been kept in hatcheries and the larvae reared in tanks at relatively warm temperatures. The idea is to rear them through the free-swimming stages, or that part of their life that is subject to the greatest dangers. It is a tricky procedure and very much like raising fish fry. The larvae are usually kept in the tanks on a diet of ground beef-liver or ground fresh mussels, until most of them cast their skin for the third time, when they are called the fourth-stage larvae. At this stage, for the first time, they look less like small pollywogs and more like small lobsters. It is about as far as they can be raised by artificial means and they are just about ready to seek the sea floor and comparative safety. But what effect the large scale plantings of lobster larvae have had through the years is difficult to say. In all probability it is very little compared with the effect of good restrictive regulation of the lobster industry. For in every alternate year an 8-inch lobster produces about 5,000 eggs, a 10-inch lobster about 10,000 eggs, a 12-inch one 20,000, and a 14-inch lobster as many as 40,000. Nature, man excluded, does pretty well when left alone, and while hatcheries do compensate for overfishing to some extent, it is better to cure that evil than to treat the symptoms, and the greater value of the hatcheries lies in the opportunities they afford for investigations into the life history, diseases, and other things we need to know.

CHAPTER THIRTEEN

SEA PLAGUE AND SEAWEED

PLAGUES have afflicted us for time out of mind. The ancient Egyptians had trouble with locusts. So do modern Egyptians and Nebraska farmers. Other plagues, more deadly but less tangible, have ranged from the Black Death of the Middle Ages to the 'flu epidemics of today. We have seen a fungus blitz the chestnut tree off the face of the North American earth, the elm and the oak are in jeopardy—and when we look to the sea the same sort of troubles exist. It would appear that the primitive forms of life, annoyed at being left behind in the somewhat dubious race towards mind and awareness, are taking out their revenge on those that have climbed out of their class. On the land and in the sea viruses, bacteria, fungi and one-celled animals have made up an army forever poised just beyond the outer lines of our defense.

The most spectacular sea plague is "red water." It comes and goes, appears here, there and anywhere, like clouds fading and reforming. The last time it broke into the news it was sweeping the Gulf Coast of Florida, and fish were dying by the millions, to be thrown up along the beaches.

The lethal organisms of "red water" are microscopic red cells called peridinians, or armored flagellates, the kind that are mainly responsible for the starry phosphorescence of the sea at night. But these particular ones seem to be as poisonous as deadly nightshade. They do not actually attack anything larger than themselves and they do not thrive at the expense of other forms, but when fish filter out microscopic animals and plants from the water passing through their gills, they have no means of keeping out the bad and retaining the good. A filter sorts according to size, but not according to taste or poisonous quality. So the fish feed, and if the water is red, they die.

A few years ago sponge fishing and sponge farming were flourishing industries in the Bahamas. Then the sponges began to wilt and rot where they stood, and despite investigations by marine biologists, nothing could be done beyond identifying the disease as an invasive fungus which rotted the sponge structure, pervading the immobile animal like the fungus blight in our chestnut. Apparently we have about as much chance of controlling the one as the other. Now and then a chestnut manages to grow to the height of a sapling and everyone holds his breath. Perhaps *this* is the resistant strain and the trees will come back to grace our avenues. But the wilting always comes, and it is much the same with sponges. Sooner or later the disease organism will be swept away, change its nature, or be killed by a change in the environment, and sponges and maybe chestnuts too will grow again.

Sometimes a disease acts so swiftly that disaster is complete before its cause is identified. This has been the tragic story of Zostera, the eel grass that used to grow in dense masses of eight-foot ribbons anchored beyond low water. It is tragic partly because it is the one flowering grass of the land which has truly invaded the sea to take its place among the ancient seaweeds. The long closely set green ribbons have composed submarine forests unique on this planet. The grass has had its commercial uses, as roof insulation and for stuffing upholstery, but no biologist that I know regrets its loss to industry. The real tragedy lies in the fact that when eel grass goes, a whole host of marine animals lose their home and many others lose their food as well.

A mysterious disease first struck the eel grass somewhere along the southern Atlantic coastline about two decades ago and swept north. After another year it appeared on the other side of the Atlantic and devastated the eel grass along the shores of the English Channel and Scandinavian waters. Only the Mediterranean and the Pacific coast remained unaffected. Biologists found both a fungus and a protozoan parasite on the diseased plants, but the suspicion remained that the real deadly organism was an invisible virus. It is more than probably true, but it is always difficult to pin down a virus, especially when the patient dies while the examination is in process.

Wherever the sea is sheltered and shallow and the force of surf and current abated, fine sediment settles down and sand becomes mixed with mud. These are the places where the eel grass flourished, in firm, muddy but not too-muddy bottoms where the long roots can ramify. And not so long ago grassy meadows could be found in all the little coves and along the margins of bays and saltwater rivers. All kinds of small marine animals lived on or among the narrow blades. When the beds were destroyed, all that depended on them went too. The wild geese and ducks migrating to and from the Canadian Arctic suddenly found only mud banks along the Nova Scotia coast in place of feeding grounds, and the Canadian Government supplied grain to help them adjust to a new situation. I remember a family of white swans in a saltwater Devonshire estuary that may have failed to survive the destruction of their Zostera beds. The parents used to trail their cygnets four miles out to sea almost into the track of ocean-going liners, and it would be good to know they still live.

In its own way a bed of eel grass is much like a jungle. If you dig into the floor of this jungle you can, or could, find brittle stars, clams and curious worms. Sea hares crawled through the stems and rare, burrowing sea anemones poked through the roots, like flowers. A number of small snails spent their lives on the blades and nowhere else, while peculiar, stalked jellyfish hung on to the waving grass. In European waters two sea creatures haunted the salt green forests like jungle beasts, taking on the stripes of their surroundings to make them invisible. Cuttlefish, no fish at all but high-powered mollusks, stalked their prey like tigers. And pipefish, relatives of the sea horse but stretched out to look like the weed itself, curled about the roots or swayed upright like the grass.

This community of life is now gone in most places. When the grass died, the sea slowly washed even the banks away, and mud sifted and drifted to other regions. Clam and scallop beds disappeared as the ground was swept from under their feet, and others suffocated as unwanted mud settled down on top of them. In a few localities clam beds flourish where earlier they produced only little runts. But sink a hole in many a present day non-productive bed and you find a layer of silt on top—and below this mud blanket lie dead clams in normal positions, all indicating a healthy population not too long ago, the maritime version of Vesuvius and Pompeii all over again.

Perhaps the worst aspect of the loss of the eel grass is the disappearance of a young-fish nursery. Large fish eat smaller fish, and the greatest mortality among fishes occurs when they first start to fight for their place in the world. The young of many an inshore fish have found the green jungle of the Zostera a haven from the rigors beyond, a nursery with abundant food. Without this margin of safety, fewer grow to maturity.

There are other submarine jungles than eel grass, though the greatest of these lie off coasts other than the North Atlantic. In cold water off California, in the Strait of Magellan, and elsewhere where cold waters well up, rich in salts from the depths, the giant brown kelp raises its broad, fifty-foot fronds on sinuous stalks a hundred and more feet long. Not only the tangled mass of jungle vegetation, but the very scale of the dense forest is reproduced, so that even the giant tuna can find food and refuge in its silent depth.

The primeval kelp forests are a world of their own, and we know too little about the life that lives within them. The kelp is no invader of the sea but has been spawned by the ocean itself and may have seen the whole marine parade of animals almost from the beginning of time.

We have found our own use for the kelp. We make agar broth out of it, the jelly that bacteriologists the world over use as a basis for culturing their precious bacteria. We extract iodine from it, and in the North Atlantic, on both sides, fisher-folk chew a purple sea lettuce as much a seaweed as the kelp, and say they like it. Like it or not, its iodine saves them from getting goiter.

Possibly the greatest use of a seaweed is made of Irish Moss, a stubby weed with short fronds, ranging from a youthful yellow-green to an old dark red purple. It forms a narrow band carpeting the sea floor from the edge of low tide to a depth of six feet below. And all along the Maritimes and Northern New England shores the weed is gathered, delivered to factories and processed. Whenever the moon is full or new, the mossers go out in their punts and skiffs and gather the moss with long-handled rakes. I have seen them returning to our cove with no more than an inch of freeboard. One moss-gathering individual recently harvested two and one half million pounds in one season. After it is dried and bleached in the sun it goes into an amazing assortment of manufactured foods, puddings, paint, shoe polish and cosmetics, anything in fact that needs a little extra substantiality. So when next you taste chocolate syrup, think of the sea moss of Maine.

CHAPTER FOURTEEN

THE ROCKLAND

THERE was a time when the rocky shore must have been bare of all living things, a time when all life was still entirely within the water. The surf broke along the rocks and left them clean.

Now, you can follow this story of rockland from an armchair and create a shore in your *mind* if you like, but I suggest you'll understand it better if you find yourself a piece of rocky coast like my own in Maine and look at it closely, when the tide is low, with both mind *and* eye. It is a heroic story—of beachheads reached and held, of pioneers established and raiders ensconced. And as it is elsewhere in the world it is the mingling of two kingdoms, the kingdom of the green and the kingdom of the quick. Like the planned storming of a beachhead, there is a rigid order of development of the shore— the plant-invaders come first, looking for sunlit positions; when they have found and established their foothold, only then does the second wave—animals—come up the rocks, seeking food and shelter.

The flowering plants of dry land are no older than butterflies, bees and birds, a mere hundred million years or so. Ten times as ancient are the microscopic one-celled marine plants that drift in the upper layers of all seas and oceans and constitute the "sea-pasture" upon which all sea life depends for its sustenance. What they must have that is not supplied by the water itself and the abundance of mineral salts therein, is light from the sun. This is available only a few hours each day, and more important, only a certain distance down from the surface, since sea water acts as a light-filter, absorbing red sunlight components within a few fathoms and blue and green light farther down. So the growth and reproduction of this individually microscopic but collectively stupendous vegetation take place at a moderate depth only, and the tiny plants live in a relatively shallow layer of surface water in which, fortunately for them, they float and drift.

But seaweeds, large and many-celled, and except for the bladder-buoyed Sargasso weed unable to float and drift, are just as dependent on the sunlight of shallow water. Further, they cannot stand a sandy or muddy shifting sea floor, or even a gravel bottom where sweeping currents roll the stones about. They must have heavy stones or submerged ledges for attachment, and that brings us back to our rocky shore. Seaweeds are essentially plants of the sea-edge where the rocks of the shoreline dip down into the sea, and those seaweeds we see exposed to the air between tides have migrated there from only as far away as those rocks that are permanently submerged.

The low-tide mark is the dividing line, and here is the choice—above the mark, the higher they go the more welcome sunlight the seaweeds get, but the greater danger there is of drying out from exposure to air, or buffeting from wind and surf; below the mark lies the greater protection of calmer water, but the deeper they go the weaker the light gets and the more difficult growth becomes.

As usual, natural selection is at work, and the seaweeds best adapted to the different levels are alive today to tell the story. Below water we find the red seaweeds, some of which look brown. These are essentially the "shade" weeds and Irish Moss is one of them. There are also true brown seaweeds that include the great kelps that form literally forests of the sea. All of these weeds merely hold on to the rocks, and what seem to be the roots are just hold-fasts, for all the plants' requirements are taken directly from the surrounding water and not up through roots as with land plants. And true seaweeds, instead of growing from the tips, grow from the base, and the tattered fronds of last year are thrown off and replaced by new growth from below.

Above the line the situation is reversed, and seaweed colonization occurs in distinct bands, each kind thriving best at its own particular combination of exposure to light and heat and duration out of water. In general these shore weeds, most of them brown seaweed (though they frequently look more olive-green or yellow), are inclined to be both leathery and tough, to resist evaporation, and are divided into many narrow fronds to resist the action of the waves like the shredded leaves of a palm tree resist the wind.

At the highest level is the Channeled Wrack, with short, many-branched fronds curling along the edge to enclose a channel. This is the most adventurous of them all, for it may be out of water for four-fifths of its life and may actually lose two-thirds of its water each time the tide goes down, to regain it when the sea returns.

Farther down we find the Flat Wrack, not unlike the first

and sometimes intermingled with it. It is exposed for two-thirds to three-quarters of its life. Then comes the broad, middle zone of the shore where the Bladder Wrack and the Knotted Wrack take over. Both have bladders filled with gas which buoy it up when the tide is in so that the whole region takes on the appearance of a small-scale submarine jungle. You don't often find the two together—the Bladder Wrack can stand a lot of wave action, while the Knotted Wrack is a plant of sheltered waters.

Finally, near the edge of low-water, the Toothed Wrack finds its place, giving way to the short carpet of Irish Moss which extends across the line and several feet below.

All the seaweeds shed their minute spores into the sea, at high tide or low, to drift where they may, and this matter too calls forth considerable reflection about the forces of natural selection at work. I imagine most of the spores start to grow. The majority fail to stick to rocks and never finding a permanent resting place finally die. But once the rocks get covered with the tiny growing spores, then selection begins to operate. Of the complicated mixture of spores that attach, for instance, in the highest levels of the shore, all die quickly from exposure when the tide goes out except those of the tough Channeled Wrack. But Channeled Wrack spores that settle lower down are faced not only with conditions that suit them less but with the intense and practically excluding competition of the Bladder or Knotted Wracks ideally suited to flourish there. The forces of wind, wave, and light efface all spores struggling to survive where they are not equipped to do so, and permit those to live that settle in what for them are the right places. Other forces have similarly molded other lives from the beginnings of time.

A jungle, whether on land or under the sea, is more than trees and undergrowth. It is food for the animal world and shelter from its enemies, living and meteorologic. So when the tide leaves "rockland," the weeds hang like drapes, fold upon fold, and behind these cool, damp curtains lie crabs and star-fishes and many others awaiting the sea's return. Without this shelter, the drying air and sun would kill them, even if the gulls who walk the weeds listening or watching for telltale sounds or movement beneath do not get them first. And some sea animals have come ashore to pasture on the rich meadows of the weed-covered rocks. These are the periwinkles, the lim-pets, and the coat-of-mail shells, or chitons.

The coat-of-mails rarely grow to more than an inch in length on the Atlantic coast, though they reach six inches in the West Indies and along the Pacific shore. They resemble their name, for in place of the usual single or double shell of the mollusk, they have eight overlapping plates. Underneath they have the same powerful muscular foot that a limpet pos-sesses, and it takes a pull equal to about seventy pounds per square inch to pull either of these animals off a rock. Chitons are a more ancient type of mollusk than limpets, but they both have the right equipment to hold on to the surfaces of rocks even under the impact of violent surf. Both have shell armor that rises to a low peak and is well designed to divert the force of a breaking wave. And both have the so-called foot, a suction muscle that can hold the shell so tightly against the rock surface that the driving water can find no leverage to lift the animal, and so merely presses it down on to the rock. Moreover, when the tide goes down, the same equipment of shell and hold-fast prevents the soft tissues from drying out, and the gills remain moist along the inner edge of the shell.

As a rule there is no sign of weed where the chitons and limpets rule, so what are they doing there? These mollusks browse on the young sporelings and filmy growths that continually strive to establish themselves on the rocks, and both animals concentrate upon their business of scraping off these minute forms of plant life about as fast as they settle. For the most part they move about at night, and then only when the tide is over them. Both exhibit a peculiar kind of homing instinct which is imperfectly understood. A limpet roams a good many inches from its base, scraping away with the ribbon of teeth in its mouth, its radula. But no matter in which direction it goes, it always returns to one particular spot to settle down, a spot where its shell fits snugly and perfectly from long usage.

Periwinkles have coiled shells, and while they might have been equally interested in eating the sporelings, their shape is too close to being spherical for them to hold on to exposed rocks entirely by their own exertions. So they specialize in living on and among the large tangles of seaweed and within sheltered crevices, browsing on the weeds, scraping off what they can, whether it is the weed itself or something growing upon it.

Periwinkles have been on the shore perhaps almost as long as the weeds themselves, at least in their modern forms, for we find a zoning of winkles almost as definite and precise as the seaweeds. There are three of them. The rough periwinkle inhabits the region from half-tide up to the splash zone. The smooth periwinkle, often a lovely yellow color, lives for the most part in the zone of the Bladder Wrack or Knotted Wrack. The large and so-called common periwinkle takes in the whole range from top to bottom.

Holding or finding a place on the shore is by no means merely a matter of having the right shape, size and strength. The individual does not last forever and in fact two or three years is quite an age for the great majority. Eggs must be spawned and fertilized in sufficient quantities to ensure that an adequate number of young shall settle in the regions where they are equipped to live, and this can be accomplished in more than one way.

The common periwinkle, like the limpet and chiton, sheds its eggs and sperm freely and independently into the sea when the tide is high and the moon is in the right phase. Eggs are produced in very large numbers, and while most of them are swept away by currents, never to return, many from their own and other localities settle on the shore after many days of drifting in the sea.

The other two winkles do the alternative, in two steps. The smooth periwinkle lays fewer, though larger, eggs and instead of throwing the precious cargo to the high seas, encloses them in small masses of jelly fastened to the weeds. Of course, when the tide goes down the egg masses may be killed by heat or drought, but those that do survive and grow are at least in the right place, and the hazards of chance dispersal are eliminated. Also, eggs that are laid in a mass must be fertilized where they are spawned, and the smooth periwinkles pair off in their own smooth periwinkle way.

This is but a step to the enterprise of the rough periwinkle, and it is characteristic of most animals that live on the highest levels of the shore. They are faced by all kinds of difficulties that can be overcome only by doing all their work at home. So in these winkles there is actual copulation, the eggs are fertilized while still within the mother and wrapped around with an egg case there and then. And to make doubly sure, the case is retained within the mantle chamber of the mother until the young are able to crawl out and start feeding beside her. The call of distant places is ignored and the rough periwinkle family is brought up domestically in its own back-yard.

The seaweeds offer more than protection and more than food—they offer position, which some people say is everything in life. Some animals seem to have little more motive than to find a smooth, soft surface on which to settle, fasten, and build. One of these, abundant along the lower levels of a weedy shore and some distance below the shore-line, is the small plume worm. Offhand it doesn't look like a worm, for the animal lives in a spirally coiled tube of lime stuck by one side to the weed. Each worm lives in its tiny tube and merely extends its pair of plumed tentacles to collect food and oxygen, while a modified tentacle forms an opercular plug that closes the tube like a cork when the worm withdraws. When the cork is in place the worm can stay wet and healthy until the tide returns.

These spiral worms do not inhabit the extreme high-shore-zone where the periwinkles live, but they are nevertheless restricted by the forces of nature to the zone they do occupy, and they are too small to spawn masses of eggs indiscriminately, in the vague hope of colonizing their own narrow belt.

So just as the periwinkle has been able to keep its young beneath its shell, the worm keeps its developing eggs in the back end of its tube. When the young emerge they are already prepared to crawl along the weed and settle down to grow a limy shell like that of their parents.

A rocky shore does not have to be a weedy shore. What lives there depends not only on the physical elements but also on who gets there first, and some animals flourish on rocks where, in the violent surf, no weed can find a footing.

The blue mussel is one of the most adept at this, and few exposed rocks and cliffs where the seas sweep and break are without a broad, blue-black band of bivalves living in apparent luxury where no other life survives. They cling to the rocks by the hundred thousands. When the water leaves them the two shells press close together and fit so well that the mollusk within is almost hermetically sealed. For a good life all that they require (aside from a few less sea gulls) is something firm to fasten to and a sweep of clean water. Stones in the mud, wharf piles or open rock all serve, and surf or a smooth, fast current are equally desirable. What, then, are they doing so high out of the water?

The answer is, I think, a multiple one. First, of course, it is because they are able to live there—they don't dry up and they can get enough food during the time they are under water. They are abundant on the open rocks because there is plenty of room—nobody else wants it. Below the tide-line space is at a premium and competition intense. And the animals that prey upon mussels (gulls excepted) can usually do it only while the tide is over them. Not all mussels can survive, let alone flourish, under such conditions. The blue and ribbed mussels can, but the large horse-mussel soon dies if the tide leaves it.

But with good footing and clear water a mussel spends many hours each day filtering the microscopic plant cells out of the water drawn over its gill curtains, in the same manner as other bivalves. And it does so very efficiently, for a single mussel passes several pints of water through its gill chamber every hour.

They shed their eggs and milt into the tide to develop as best they can. The numbers are enormous, and you have only to look at submerged surfaces where seed mussel have recently settled to appreciate the unbelievable ranks of potential settlers there must be swimming about in the sea during the breeding season. And they grow quickly once they settle, with an inevitable weeding out due to over-crowding. When the Island of Walcheren in the Netherlands was recaptured from the Germans towards the end of the last war, the dykes had been breached and the sea had flooded the island. A year later, when the dykes were mended and the water pumped out, the roads, houses, fences and even the trees were smothered in a blue carpet of mussels.

Pull a mussel and you find it comes away with a breaking of a cluster of strong threads collectively called the byssus. These are like the threads of the cloth-of-gold byssus of the pen-shells to the south. The mussel produces them by causing a sticky fluid to run down a narrow groove in its foot which solidifies on exposure to the water or the air. It is in fact a true plastic, and the animal uses the threads for anchorage to the rock surface. As a rule the anchoring attachments are

F

spread out like the guy ropes of a tent. If some break, new
ones are quickly formed. In fact young mussels readily change
their position by a process of mountain-climbing with the aid
of these ropes. Threads are attached and the mussel hauls itself
up. The foot fastens new ones where it could not reach before,
and by a slow, laborious but very sure method, the animal can
adjust its position to ensure the best combination of safety
and feeding facilities.

Sometimes a large mussel, particularly a horse-mussel, may
have an uninvited companion. There is a little pea-crab that
takes up housekeeping within the shells of living mussels.
Curiously, only the female does this and as far as we know
she never leaves the safety of her room. It is doubtful whether
the mussel suffers very much from the intruder, but there is
no doubt that the crab benefits greatly, and more than in a
matter of shelter. An investigator cut a window in one of the
shells of an occupied mussel to see just what went on. The
pea-crab sat happily in the middle with a pair of mussel gill
curtains on each side of it, where it could scrape its claws over
the gills to collect and transfer to its own mouth the food that
was sliding toward the mouth of the mussel.

The female pea-crab is soft, weak and gentle, and outside
the mussel would have short shrift indeed. For many years
the male seemed to be a mysterious, unknown stranger, but
eventually he was caught visiting his wife. It wasn't that the
male crab was rare. It was simply that he was so different
from his spouse he had been classed as a different kind of crab
altogether and had not been recognized. Apart from looks he
is smaller and lives an active, independent life, as many males
are inclined to do. Running in and out of mussels is less haz-

ardous than it seems, for the male is a tough-shelled little cus-
tomer that wouldn't be particularly bothered by the nip of
mussel valves.

When it comes to sitting on a rock and gaining the necessi-
ties of life from a rising tide, the barnacle does as well as the
mussel and does it in its own way with its own equipment. As
long as I can remember, from my pre-school rambles on a
Cornish coast to watching my own children on the rocky coast
of Maine, barnacles, mussels and limpets have been cutting
my feet and ruining the seat of my pants. The barnacles
looked like limpets and seemed to have the shells of mollusks.
I know now that they aren't mollusks, but what they are has
never been obvious.

Look at a rock barnacle out of water. You see a shell of lime
shaped very much like a miniature volcano, with ramparts
along the rim of the slopes. In the center where the crater
should be are the two valves, held together so that water
within cannot escape. Now, none of this suggests what kind of
animal lies within, but if the tide comes up or if the barnacle
is within a little pool, you can see a strange event. The two
valves open and a ghostlike hand protrudes and fans the
water urgently. In a second it is gone, but in a moment or two
the valves open again and once more the hand comes out. It
is rather as if its owner were casting a net through the water
in the blind hope of catching some microscopic edibles, dead
or alive.

The barnacle situation is a curious one, almost as curious
as if a bird became stuck to its nest and gained nourishment
by beating insects into its mouth with its wings.

For our barnacle is no mollusk, but a true crustacean, descendant of ancestors that swam actively in the sea and didn't cling stubbornly to rocks. The internal structure of the animal is clearly crustacean and would convince any student, and the offspring are a dead give-away. The eggs develop into the nauplius larva, typical of most crustaceans and nothing else. The nauplius larva transforms into the cypris larva after a certain amount of growth. This still swims about the sea like its ancestors by means of six pairs of swimming appendages protected by a pair of plastic shells. At this stage it is not only obviously crustacean but it is a special kind of crustacean from which the larva gets its name.

After a short life in this form, the larvae attach themselves by their front end to the rocks, feeling for a suitable spot with their antennae and then secreting a cement which will anchor them to that particular place for the rest of their life. Gradually more and more lime is produced around the animal until it is safely imprisoned in its own fortress. Inside, the crustacean, fastened to the ground by the neck, lies on its back with its six pairs of feet pointed toward the roof. And when the two central shells are opened, the group of feet extend as a unit through the opening and fan away, pulling in a handful of water, with or without food, toward the mouth.

You might say that the barnacle, lying on its back and kicking food into its mouth, is doing its best to live like a mussel, but it is none-the-less crustacean, though it has to a certain extent suffered the mussel's fate. Remember the man who had one talent which he failed to use and had taken away from him? Mussels and barnacles are without much doubt the descendants of mollusks and crustaceans that at one time were much more active and had brains of a sort. Heads and their accessories evolved to enable animals to sense and control where they were going. If they go nowhere there is nothing left for a head to do. To put it briefly, mussels and barnacles have lost their heads. They have no eyes, no organs of balance, no tentacles; and as usual when senses close down, little goes on.

Yet barnacles cannot get away from their own nature. They are born crustacean and they stay crustacean. And like all crustaceans their skin is inelastic and has to be cast off periodically for growth to continue. At times the shallow sea is thick with the cast molts of barnacles. Unlike most crustaceans, however, barnacles are hermaphrodites, that is, both male and female glands function in every individual. This may have become essential to barnacle life, because of a crustacean habit that seems to be a liability under the circumstances. Crustacean eggs have to be fertilized before their tough membranes are formed about them, that is, before they are laid, and so copulation is a necessary procedure. And in spite of the fact that mature barnacles cannot move about at all, they still have to fertilize the eggs by a process of coupling. Breeding barnacles extend a long tube through the valves to reach over to deposit sperm within a nearby barnacle. Unless they are closely packed together they cannot reach far enough, and a solitary barnacle is fated to remain both a bachelor and an old maid at the same time. When eggs are successfully fertilized, they develop slowly to the swimming stage safely within the parental castle.

Seaweeds, plume worms, barnacles and mussels all thrive in "rockland" and for very much the same kind of reasons. Each is there about its own business and apart from a certain jostling for space, they do unto others as they would be done by. Periwinkles have colonized the shore because they are vegetarians and the weeds are there for them to eat. But it would be too much to expect the filter-feeding animals to be left alone. The dog whelk has followed them ashore.

Dog whelks are much the same as other whelks, except that they are small and look somewhat like periwinkles. Like all whelks and winkles they have the shield-like operculum on the back end of the crawling foot, with which they seal off the opening of the shell when the animal is withdrawn. And they have a long breathing siphon that has come from the ancestral habit of plowing through sand and mud in search for food while simultaneously needing clean water for the gill chamber. On the shore this is unnecessary, but they still have it, and it tells something of their past. Dog whelks have the standard whelk equipment for boring holes in bivalves, but they have less need of it since mussels and barnacles are relatively defenseless. Old mussels are drilled in the usual whelk manner, but young ones are eaten usually by simply forcing the shells apart. And there is a lot of rich meat in a mussel. You can generally tell whether a dog whelk has been feeding on mussels by the color of its shell, a dark-brown or pinkish-purple. When they feed on barnacles their shells are white. A yellow shell means exposure to wave action.

No boring is necessary for feeding on barnacles. The valves are easily forced apart, the mouth tube inserted and the tissues within soon digested. The whelk does produce a purple dye called purpurin, which is poisonous, and it may well be a weapon of chemical warfare, used to kill the barnacle and cause the muscles to relax. Long ago men extracted the color to dye the royal purple robes of Emperors and Kings.

As a rule the dog whelks feed on the barnacles till the supply runs low, and then switch to a diet of mussels. When they do it seems they have to learn new ways and it takes a little time. But it is interesting and significant that a little dog whelk with its infinitesimal brain can accomplish something that we recognize as adaptive learning! When you find a pretty little black dog whelk shell with white bands running through it, you will know it is a mussel-eater that had to turn to barnacles once in a while and had a little trouble learning how to do it.

Dog whelks are as fully adjusted to shore life as the rough periwinkle, for their young hatch as miniature adults alongside the parents, and there is no adventuring to drift out into a wet and watery wilderness.

The little egg capsules, each like a grain of wheat, are a common sight, attached in rows and clusters within sheltered crevices and behind curtains of seaweed. They are made at the rate of about one each hour, up to about thirty in a sitting. Within each case some hundreds of yolky eggs are encased. And here again we find whelk nature retained in all its detail. For like many others of this kind, only a few of the eggs within each capsule are fertilized and undergo development. When they hatch out of their egg membranes, still within the capsule, they find a ready-made store of food in the undeveloped eggs. They actually emerge only after some months, and when they finally do leave the capsules they are small whelks able to crawl along and keep to the shore. The only difference in their habits is that they live lower down, and start life by feeding, not on barnacles and mussels, but on the minute plume worms in their spiral coils on the weeds and rock. Not till the whelks have grown to a much larger size do they venture up the shore to the middle zone for bigger game.

CHAPTER FIFTEEN

ROCKPOOLS

Much of my youth was spent on the coast of South Devon, near Salcombe, a salt-water estuary lying between 400-foot headlands that stick far out into the English Channel, where I saw the last of the Finnish five-masted barquentines fail to keep clear and come to a tragic end on the rocks. The rockpools along this coast are beautiful and well-known, and the seeds of my interest in the sea and its life were planted during these visits.

I can think of no better place than rockpools to begin the study of marine life, for these undersea worlds-in-miniature left by the ebbing tide in every deep and shallow depression in rock or sand can show you much of the way animals left behind there adjust, or fail to adjust, to differences in their natural environment—differences sometimes better shown in the rockpool than elsewhere because time and change come so quickly.

It is the time the pool is left as a pool that matters, and this depends on its height above low water and the size of the tide-rise. Once a pool has been left by the tide changes go on in its water, and the longer it is left the more extreme these changes become. In the highest pools along a rocky shore the water will be warm to your hand, especially on a sunny day and the chances are there will be a white rim of brine salt around the edge where the water has evaporated. Half-way down the shore the pools will be larger and deeper, with no white salt about the edge. Seaweeds may grow thickly in them, but as a rule only a few animals will be found, periwinkles, barnacles and one or two crustacean side-swimmers, for the pools are still likely to be too-long left by the tide and too warm, and the weeds may have changed the complex chemistry of the sea water, making it much too alkaline for animal comfort.

But as we get down to the lower reaches, where they are abandoned only a short time by the tide, the pools are more and more entrancing until they become, in microcosm, the undersea world itself, its animal and plant life almost intact. Deep pools sheltered by overhanging ledges far down near the edge of low water stay cool and even cold an inch beneath the surface. Then the weeds are all to the good—they haven't had time to change the alkalinity of the water and they increase the shaded coolness and give shelter in other ways. If you look into a pool like this and comprehend what you see, including the brooding reflection of your own face, you will embrace the universe—for the beginning and end of living time are there before you.

When you climb down the rocks and look into a pool you have a feeling of personal discovery. It is justified in a sense, for that pool is not the same pool that was there yesterday. The water has been changed. Some animals have left and others have come into it, and still others have undergone a sea change. But although it has changed and is now your pool, a pool was there yesterday and every day for years and possibly centuries. The spirit of the pool, giving it its rich interest and beauty, has lived along rocky shores for time out of mind, and we are not the first to have felt it.

A century ago the general theory of evolution was launched by Darwin and Wallace into a startled but subconsciously waiting world. Today we are passing from the question of whether evolution has occurred or not to the more significant one concerning evolution's meaning. In reading the literature of biology you often get the feeling that the Darwinian theory burst like a bomb-shell into a society that had its mind on other matters entirely. This is not so. Their mid-century generalizations were simply the culmination of intense popular interest in natural history. In zoology, botany and geology by far the most inspiring efforts were made by amateurs, to whom the contemplation and recording of natural phenomena were hobbies and not means to a livelihood. Clergymen and country squires, writers and merchants had sufficient leisure in an unhurried world to look about them, to see with the mind as well as the eye; and it is here that the roots of modern biology lie and from here that our sustenance must come. The distinction today between professional and amateur and the current belief that science is purely a matter of white coats and laboratory benches are things to be deplored, for it is outside the ranks of the orthodox that new visions arise. A tide-pool, research-center for amateur and professional alike, is as provocative a piece of the evolving universe as any, and small enough not to be overwhelming.

Historically, we tend to think of the Mid-Victorians as rather pompous folk who wore "wide-awakes" and loose, black coats and dressed small boys in petticoats. Yet I don't believe there is any great difference between a naturalist now who wears a shirt, shorts and sneakers and the great Professor Louis Agassiz, who lived in a Boston where clipper-ships graced the harbor. He had this to say of pools: "He who would make a successful search after these delicate specimens, and discriminate carefully between them, must not be over-fastidious in his examination of the puddles and tide-pools among the rocks. He must go prepared to lie down, sometimes to stand almost upon his head, to creep up and down through wet and slimy crevices, and over the surfaces of treacherous rocks, covered with seaweed." And the Back Bay thoroughbreds followed him around.

But rockpools first came into their biological own not along the New England coast but the southwest shores of England. Philip Gosse belonged to the same period as Agassiz but he traveled a different circuit. He left Dorset on the English Channel in 1827 for Newfoundland, farmed in Canada, taught school in Alabama, returned to England for awhile, and then went bird collecting in Jamaica, returning to London and finally settling on the coast of Devon to become a world-famous artist-naturalist-writer. He wrote book after book, superbly illustrated, on the wonders and beauty of seashore animals, particularly those of the rockpools, and became so popular that he conducted shore classes with excited, respectable, over-dressed, middle aged Mid-Victorians during the same years Agassiz held his own classes on Pekinese Island off the coast of New England.

It was Gosse who carried his enterprise and enthusiasm to their logical conclusion and started the fad for marine aquaria by publishing a handbook on how to maintain aquaria in the home, and even how to manufacture artificial sea water out of table salt, magnesium and potassium chloride and Epsom salts. He introduced the idea of the balanced aquarium in which filmy seaweeds offset the sea animals by giving off oxygen and taking up carbon dioxide, so that their requirements dove-tailed, or so he thought.

All of this public interest led to several consequences. One, which Gosse regretted bitterly, was that armies of collectors, armed with buckets and spades, hammers and chisels, and boys to carry the loot, invaded the lower beaches and stripped the pools of their inhabitants. He felt it might be centuries before the injury would heal. This was the bad side of it. The good side came to those who kept a salt water aquarium and faithfully observed and wrote down what went on in it. For them, as for the many who have kept aquaria since, natural events took place that could not otherwise be seen by an air-breathing human being. A greater consequence was the expansion of the small, home aquarium into large municipal aquaria, in London, Brighton, and later in Naples, New York and many other cities. The world beneath the sea, in much of its fantasy and color, emerged before the unbelieving eyes of the stay-at-home city folk, to their continual delight and entertainment.

I have known many rockpools, in several lands and both hemispheres, and no two have ever been alike. Each had its own wonder. Why does a pool hold things its does, why are other sea creatures and seaweeds not there, who visits the pool when it is a pool no longer and just a weedy hollow in the sea

floor? A pool teems with questions and most of them have
yet to be answered.

I remember pools in South Devon that had sea wrack above
the water line only, the pool itself like a bathtub lined with
pink enamel, really a pink encrusting coralline seaweed, with
green, flower-like snake-lock anemones like a Gorgon's head,
and darting little brown fish never more than an inch in
length. The anemones never seemed to catch the fish, and yet
they flourished and grew, while the young fish were always
there. The anemones were the same that were there the day
before, but the fish visited from pool-hollow to pool-hollow
when the tide was high and no one could tell the difference.

But the pools on Ocean Point in Maine that I have been
working most during the last few years are different, large
and deep, thick with yellow-brown kelps, and icy-cold a foot
below the surface. When you part the weed, and look into
the depths when the rippled surface is still again, a fairyland
appears in the shafted sunlight reaching down between the
stalks of the kelp.

The sea plants alone give an abundance of color, a varied
foliage and a range of size, from the yellow-brown of the
broad-bladed kelp, and the delicate dark-red and light-green
shade weed and sea lettuce, to the thick, miniature limy-pink
trees of coralline. But the blue-green and yellow, and yellow-
green meadow from which they all arise is no plant at all but
a sponge, entirely animal for all its immobility and vegetable
appearance. This sponge of the pools is the Crumb-o'-bread
Sponge and as much a sponge as the giant Loggerhead Vase.
But like most sponges of the shore region, it has no very definite shape. A stalked vase can live safely only in fairly quiet

water, and where waves are often violent, sponges and many other growths, whether plant or animal, cling to the rocks and spread out as much like a film or crust as possible. And the hole at the summit of each conical mound of the encrusting mass is no mouth but merely allows water to escape from within. The water gets in by filtering through the sponge surface, drawn in by the sponge lining, and leaves its microscopic organisms within the sponge tissues as food.

When you look more carefully where the kelp hold-fasts interrupt the sponge carpet you see other colors and patterns. Brittle stars and serpent stars, their five arms in a sinuous and sinister movement, cluster together, probing here and there and within the sponge cavities for any meat they can find. Each star has a central disk, often vivid in pattern and bright in color, and painted bands along the arms. When mussels are in the pool, as they are here, both the horse-mussel and the blue, starfish are also common, clinging tightly to the rocky walls or in the crevices, busy opening and eating the bivalves. It is probably a case of smothering against muscle pull. A mussel holds its shells pretty tightly together, but a starfish fastens its tube feet to both shells, more or less smothering the bivalve, and as the valves open a slit to get water, in go the digestive juices of the starfish, containing a powerful corrosive and paralyzing agent. Then the starfish, which has a small mouth and no teeth, extrudes its thin membranous stomach outside of its own body, wraps it around the mussel meat and digests it within the mussel's own shell.

Anytime you pick up a starfish and keep it out of water for five minutes, you find it goes limp and flaccid. The hydraulic output goes on but the intake is cut off. There is a hard round plate or stone imbedded in the top center region of the starfish which is easy to see, and this is the water intake. Essentially it is a filter which allows water to pass in, sterilizing it in the process. Inside the animal the water flows into a ring tube that supplies the five main conduits passing up the five arms. From each of these, pairs of muscular bladders receive water, and each bladder controls the tube and suction-disk that protrudes outside the arm. With this equipment, unique in the animal kingdom, the starfish and its relations walk and feed.

My pool narrows at one end between converging ledges and I can reach along the bottom without actually standing in the water. Sea urchins browse along the lower sides of the rock, grinding off the calcareous vegetation. Though they look like a spine-covered baseball they belong with the starfishes in the "group of five," the Echinoderms or spiny-skinned. All their structures are arranged in five rays about a center, even the fantastic teeth, five of them forming the Lantern of Aristotle, the first observer to describe them. The same hydraulic system is used, a stone filter, ring tube and five conduits, and double rows of sucker-equipped tube feet. The spines carry the weight of the ball of the body and the flexible feet warp the animal slowly along. Crevices are popular with them, for a round, rigid, ball-shaped animal is easily disturbed by waves, and narrow places offer security. Calcareous seaweeds are necessary as food, since so much lime has to go into the formation and growth of their shell. You may have seen these shells cast up on a beach, with the spines and living tissue that covered it rubbed off. The whole structure is a wonderful inlay of closely

placed polygonal plates, so tightly fitted that a hard solid wall
is formed, perforated only by minute holes for the protrusion
of the tube feet.

Sometimes you can find young sea cucumbers in the same
crevices with the sea urchins. They are echinoderms also and
specialists in crevice-crawling. The large calcareous plates of
the urchin are reduced to microscopic bodies in their leathery,
cucumber-shaped body wall and in no way interfere with its
flexibility. But the tube feet and the hydraulic system remain
for anchoring the animal in its groove. Whether teeth were
ever present is doubtful, for these animals feed in a manner
very different from the brittle stars, starfish and urchins. Their
five double tentacles collect microscopic food particles from
the water, and they inhabit the rocky cracks simply for shelter.
It is curious that in almost any of these low-water pools you
can find these four kinds of echinoderm animals, curious for
apart from deep-water sea lilies these are the only four types
of the "group of five" still surviving on the planet. They are
so different among themselves, yet each kind finds its own
way of living, growing and reproducing within the small pool-
universe.

There is other animal life in the pool. Dahlia anemones hug
the cracks, half buried in sand at the bottom, with a firm hold
on the rock beneath. Shore crabs haunt the weed forest, and
you have to see one in such a setting to realize the perfection
of its camouflage. Prawns, like translucent shrimp, dart back
into the corners at the least disturbance. And last, but by no
means least in either interest or beauty, the delicate fronds of
hydroids invest the stems of red and brown weeds alike, feathery, branching growths that belie their animal nature. These

are colonial creatures, the tip of each little branch resembling
a sea anemone in miniature and feeding in essentially the same
way with its circle of tentacles. They are in fact related.

And sometimes, if your eyesight and patience are good, you
can see these hydroids setting free small, swimming jellyfish
by the hundred, for it is only these mobile members of the
hydroid colony that grow to an appreciable size and become
sexually mature. When the tide returns they are swept out to
sea and there they drift and grow through all the long winter
months, to send forth their seed and as hydroids recolonize
the rockpools along the shore.

CHAPTER SIXTEEN

THE MINERS

THE shallow sea and the shore, for all their silence and watery mystery, have much in common with a jungle. Intensity of competition has driven life to evolve into many strange and fantastic forms, and sent many animals in search of a safe retreat above all else. Filter-feeders like the bivalves are hard put to carry on their own quiet, efficient business of taking invisible organisms out of the water. They are the grazing animals of the sea, and hunters are all about them.

Escape has been found in two ways. Along the shore, the farther down the better and especially below the tide, you can usually find large boulders resting on rock or other stones so that narrow spaces lie between the under surface and the sea floor. Water flows freely beneath, and while it is not exactly a vast flatland like the sand and mud-flats, it is a land of surfaces. Large animals cannot crawl beneath such low ceilings, and anything that can live there is fairly immune from attack. In most parts of the world, if you turn over the largest rock you can move, you may with luck find most of the lower animal kingdom spread out before you.

It is mostly an encrusting kind of kingdom, spreading out as much as possible to take advantage of surface, pretending that the third dimension does not exist. Two-dimensional sponges cover enormous areas, coloring the rock with yellows, reds, oranges and greens. About as thin as the sponges and making patches of color of about the same size, the golden-star tunicate, Botryllus, makes star-spangled mats. It is hard to believe that these mats claim closer relationship to you than they do to the sponge. And hanging in feathery draperies wherever they can find and keep a foothold, hydroids and sea mats wave gently in the water.

It all looks safe enough, but even here the predators get in. One kind in particular has specialized in penetrating this stony underworld to feed upon the inmates and to lay its own eggs in stone-fastened security. It is not merely a matter of being flat enough to crawl into this little world. It is necessary to eat what is there, and in all candor there are very few animals that do have a taste for sponge, hydroids, or tunicates. Hydroids, like their anemone relatives, have poisonous stinging cells, and a little poison in your dinner goes a long way. Why tunicates, whether they be sea squirts or golden stars, are generally left alone I do not know, unless it be their indigestible outer-coat of thick cellulose.

Yet, surprisingly, there is one group of animals that feeds and flourishes on a diet of all three, though even among this small group there are specialists, hydroid-eaters, sponge-eaters, and sea squirt-eaters. These are the sea slugs. The name is accurate but aesthetically unfortunate. They are slugs it is true, for like the somewhat repulsive land slugs they are snails that discard their shells when almost too small to see. But unlike their landed relatives the sea slugs are not particularly slimy, and they are among the most beautiful animals in the sea, both in color and shape. They glide into the crevices, bearing branching, brightly colored living structures where the shell should be, each to feed on its own choice of the more immobile but equally colorful victims. In season each lays its coils or curtains of eggs in jelly, securely anchored to the rocks.

It is no great step from encrusting a rock to boring into it, though it is a little startling to think of the sponge as a boring animal. Yet some kinds of sponges bore or etch holes in rocks and in the shells of oysters and clams. Probably the lime of the shell is dissolved by acid, so that the living sponge tissue sinks below the surface. Why, I do not know. I cannot see how it would make much difference to an encrusting sponge whether it is surface or subsurface. More than likely it simply does not matter, and it may be an unimportant consequence of an unusual acidity in the tissues of certain sponges. Unimportant that is, to everyone but the oyster, who probably feels it rather deeply.

The real rock-borers, however, are bivalves themselves. A pair of shells held together by powerful muscles can be employed for more than protection, and several clams have undertaken a spectacular form of engineering, some specializing in rock-drilling and others in wood. These are the piddocks and shipworms, and they play their part in a changing world. Piddocks bore into, and honeycomb, the bases of cliffs until the overhangs finally fall into the sea. In the course of a few million years you might be surprised what they could do to a coast line. As for the shipworm, as much a mollusk as any oyster, many a mariner has rued its existence. Sir Francis Drake ravaged the Spanish fleet, but it was the shipworm that finally destroyed the *Golden Hind*.

Piddocks are boring clams with shells surprisingly thin and brittle considering the work they do. Some burrow into stiff clay, but others think nothing of drilling their way into concrete piling. All of it is done by mechanical drilling and not by any use of acids.

Ordinary bivalves have a ligament that binds the two shells together at the hinge. This is lacking in the piddock and the shells are free to move in a sort of rocking action, under the influence of the large powerful muscles within. The foot of the animal gets a good grip on the wall of the burrow, the shells are parted under the pull of the muscle, and sharp teeth like a saw on the deep end of the shells scrape away at the rock. Slowly but inexorably the mollusk grinds its way deeper and deeper. The action is much like that of a steam shovel.

What does seem to be pure luxury under the circumstances is that the piddock, living in perpetual darkness in its own tight-fitting prison, exudes a slime that gives off a vivid greenish-blue light. No one has yet thought of any possible value it may have for the piddock. Having no eyes the piddock cannot even see itself shine, unless the whole animal in some way feels the proud glow of its own radiance.

What does a boring piddock do when it runs head on into another piddock boring in the opposite direction? The result is one piddock less, unless they are evenly matched, in which case it could be two piddocks less. Otherwise the stronger keeps on drilling and tunneling, and grinds its way right through the weaker. It is just from habit, for none of this is concerned with food, merely safety. The opposite end of the animal, like that of any other bivalve, draws in a current of water for both food and oxygen.

A piddock will turn aside from wood in order to keep to stonework. That is its masochistic privilege, and there is no accounting for taste. Shipworms on the other hand stick to wood and can so riddle a timber that it finally falls apart. Probably because they look less like the mollusks they are than do any others, they were not recognized as such until the eighteenth century. For all that, they have been known to all sailors for a long time, and known only too well. Roman galleys and Greek triremes disintegrated as the planking became riddled, and when the dykes of Holland were attacked by shipworm a couple of centuries ago, the country itself was put in jeopardy. Its name is Teredo and it is quite an amazing animal.

Teredo's minute, two-shelled larvae swim in the sea like those of most other bivalves from whom they are difficult to tell apart. When they come up against a wooden surface they hang on with a byssus thread, just like a mussel. Then the shells grow into a different shape and quickly become an extremely efficient cutting tool with blade-like edges, rocking ball-joints, and strong muscles for operating. The whole machinery scrapes and slices as it is swung alternating right and left through 180 degrees to cut a smooth circular burrow through the wood.

When a piddock drives into rock or clay, the whole animal moves into the burrow and does not change its shape. But a Teredo fastens the ends of its water siphons to the outer opening of the wood, and as the other end cuts and bores deeper and deeper, the body in between lengthens to keep its two ends connected, which is what gives it the long tubular shape of a worm. It is a neat trick if you can do it, and there is method in it—the shipworm has a pair of limy pallets at the outer end and can close the entrance of the burrow with them, thereby sealing the animal and the water inside. By this means it can survive even for weeks when the wood is out of water. Sooner or later however, the passage must be opened for an exchange of stale water for new. This is mainly to gain oxygen, not food, for while the Teredo can still feed in the old-fashioned bivalve way by filtering minute organisms out of the water current, it can also digest and nourish itself on the wood it shreds. This is no mean undertaking. It is not just a matter of passing wood fragments into the mouth and through the intestine, but of actually digesting them, and this is something very few animals have succeeded in doing. Only Teredo, a few land snails and wood-boring insects are able to digest the cellulose of wood and turn it into soluble sugar to be used to supply the body with fuel and energy.

Teredo is as blind as the piddock, but what sense it is that enables shipworms to burrow into a piece of wood until it is virtually all Teredo and no wood, without entering the lime-lined burrows of their neighbors is hard to say, unless it is the lime itself.

Another marine wood-borer with a decided predilection for wharf piles is the gribble, no mollusk but a small crustacean belonging to the same group as the sand-hoppers and side-swimmers. It is less than a quarter inch long and it has seven pairs of short clawed legs. It has also a pair of rasp-and-file mandibles that chew readily into wood. Burrows are generally superficial, but in the course of time so much wood can be eaten away, layer by layer, that wharves eventually collapse, piles completely eaten through at the water line.

Each little gribble hole usually contains two gribbles. As usual, the one doing all the work at the blind end of the burrow is sure to be the female, and she not only does it all but most of the time she carries around with her twenty to thirty eggs developing in a brood pouch. When the eggs hatch, the youngsters set to work at once on their own to make little burrows alongside their mamma's. All the usual hazards of growing up seem to have been overcome, and there seems to be no limit to the numbers of young gribbles that can be safely born and raised, except that wood that stands or floats in the sea is decidedly limited, and sooner or later the gribbles eat themselves out of house and home and the gribble population, alas, diminishes.

Wharf piles are often as closely occupied as any rocky shore, for most marine animals and seaweeds that can anchor themselves to rock and draw their sustenance from the sea can do so just as well on wood or concrete pillars. Even better than the wharf piles, which dry out with the fall of the tide, are the floats. As a rule the side of a float next to a wharf is always in shade and quiet water, and even more so is the underside of the float itself. These are places where there is usually a rich growth of organisms, especially if the floats are not dragged ashore to be scraped and painted every year. This procedure may extend the life of a float and gratify its owner, but it is an exasperation to a marine naturalist. I have found many of the animals I have most needed by lying flat on a float and reaching down and under with blind fingers for come what may—thick clusters of Tubularia and other hydroids that look like bouquets of small flowers; anemones in green, pink, marbled peach-and-white, or orange that grow between masses of dark blue mussels; long fronds of kelp hanging down from the sea garden into the green depths. Everything seems upside-down and you are lying where the soil should be and the sky is deep in the sea. Often the kelp blades are highly decorated, sometimes with every inch of space matted over with green, yellow and blue carpeting of the golden-star tunicate and frosted tapestry of sea mat. Skeleton shrimps also hang from the finer weeds, fantastic little creatures rarely longer than an inch that hang by their tails, swaying with the weed and clutching with minute but fearsome claws at any small passer-by. Even a jellyfish has found it easier to hang by a stalk than to swim forever struggling against the pull of gravity, fishing for its food with eight clusters of tentacles ready to give a deathly embrace to any wanderer that swims too close.

CHAPTER SEVENTEEN

THE HEAD OF THE COVE

OUR cove, Lobster Cove in Linekin Bay, Maine, is a quiet, secluded place where the winds cannot reach and the tide flows quietly in and as quietly ebbs. When the tide is high you can row a skiff into still waters that reflect the deep greens of the spruce along the shore and the warmer colors of the lichen-covered rocks. It is a time to look into the water for little moving spots or larger blobs of clearness. For when all is still and smooth and unrippled, delicate sea things come close to the surface where they can be seen. Little silver-black dots glinting in the light are the eyes of fish fry drifting inshore on the flood, and if you can look close enough you can see the brain between the eyes, through the transparent skull. Red dots may mean many things, from small crustacean copepods, the "red feed" itself, or an oceanic siphonophore resembling a string of jellyfish threaded together, with long red-dotted fishing lines drifting behind.

Clear disturbances, with iridescent ripples, are fascinating if you can dip one or two out into a glass jar, for they are almost sure to be comb jellies, again resembling jellyfish though even less closely related. A jellyfish forever contracts and relaxes the margin of its bell as it pulses through the water, whereas a comb jelly glides like a zeppelin, propelled by eight rows of infinitesimal light-catching oars along its sides. And of course you may actually have a jellyfish, for when it comes to small ones, early in the season, they are legion and a joy to watch.

When the tide goes out, the same quietness of the waters leaves animals almost unaware of the ebb, and you can find them on the muddy sand in an inch or so of water right up to the edge. There are more than you can see. Many are the color of the sand, and some burrow down till they are flush with the surface. Yet if you wade with bare feet, that constant flicking against your skin is shrimp jumping out of the way at the last moment, hardly to be seen even when you look at them, each like a small gray lobster without the latter's oversized claws. Some will be "in berry," carrying the developing eggs beneath the tail like most of their kind. The egg carriers are always the largest—for small shrimps are male and each male becomes a female as it grows up.

Sand dabs and young flounder dart away as your foot descends upon them. Their camouflage is so perfect you do not see them till they move, and you lose sight of them when they settle again. I have never succeeded in stepping on one even when I knew where to step, and it can become a very frustrating, though non-competitive, sport. If the fish move to a place where the ground pattern is different, it takes only a few minutes for the body color and pattern to conform to the new surroundings and regain invisibility. All this change is effected through their eyes, which in some manner reflect the essential environmental patterns into the nervous system where nerves and chemical messengers regulate the size and color of the pigment spots over the body surface. This is true only for the upper surface; the underneath side remains white.

So we come to the true nature of these flat fish. They lie on one side, some kinds on the right, others on the left, and there is more to it than the mere matter of becoming more pigmented on one side than the other. Even if a fish is flattened from side to side, as many are, the business of lying flat on the sea floor leaves but one eye in a seeing position and the other buried in mud or sand. Unless of course the fish should be a flounder, a sole, plaice or halibut. In these and some others we find a curious occurrence. The young fish swim in the upper water like most young fish. But just before they are ready to go down to the bottom, one eye migrates slowly across the bridge of the nose, coming to rest on the same side of the head as the other. Not only that, but the nose skeleton, which would ordinarily be in the way, dissolves and leaves a passage for the eye to take even before the movement begins. Finally, the young flat fish lies with one blind white side against the sea floor, and the other side pigmented and looking up into the watery world with both the left and the right eye.

Head Cove is flatland when the tide is out, and only the sand and mud-flats have meaning. Dark, purple-brown sand dollars lie thickly here and there, like beds of flowers of another world. With a shell so thick and so flat it is hard to see how the equipment of this sea urchin can be so encompassed. A bed of round purple dollars seems entirely immobile, with individual movements so subtle that it is difficult to keep your eye upon any one of them. But when a predatory starfish crosses a bed it is as though a cloth had been wiped across a slate. The dollars lying in the path and for a foot or so on each side sink quickly below the surface of the sand. Something like a sense of smell or taste must warn them, and the operation itself, conducted by a brainless organism, is almost incomprehensible.

These are the flatlanders, though others are there as well. Scavengers abound, for there is usually good picking, both animal and vegetal, where the water draws back from creek and cove. The common periwinkles and small whelks are so abundant that you cannot walk in the water without stepping on them by the dozen.

Abundant too are the hermit crabs, for empty snail-shell homes are there for the taking, and food not too difficult to find. They are ridiculous creatures, all front and no fortitude, with all the pugnacity and nervousness of a coward, weapons and armor in front and only vulnerable tenderness behind. Hence the snail shell—a hermit crab walking without one would not last for two minutes. They are only safe as long as their soft abdomens are tucked away within the coil of an empty shell. Then they are fully protected, and a hermit withdrawn is an impregnable fortress of molluscan shell and heavy crustacean armor.

Their eggs are laid and incubated within their foster-home and have nothing to fear until they hatch, or until the mother finds the quarters too cramped. A hermit not only has to cast its own skin periodically, as do all crustaceans, but it has to find a new, unoccupied and larger snail shell whenever the old one gets to be too tight. This means leaving the old for the new, not a lengthy procedure but an exceedingly dangerous one for all that. It has to make sure that the new shell will be large enough; sometimes mistakes are made and only discovered when it is out of the old and halfway into the new. And it must be sure that no worm or other irritating inmate is not already far inside the new shell, which demands a careful preliminary exploration. When all seems to be in order there is a hasty abandonment of the old shell and an equally hasty and undignified scramble into the new. If other hermits are within striking distance they make a violent effort to catch their neighbor at moving time, and if they succeed the neighbor is eaten.

Where hermits are common, a few nearly always have a pink or orange covering, not on the crab itself but on the shell of its mollusk home. These coverings are carpets of hydroids that seem to flourish only on snail shells that are dragged around by hermits, very rarely on shells containing the original owner. The hydroid settles on the colony in spite of anything the hermit can do about it. On the other hand, there is a hermit crab in the south and other places, in somewhat deeper water, that plucks a certain kind of sea anemone from a stone and holds it firmly to the shell it lives in until the anemone fastens itself. What advantage it gets from this sort of arrangement is not easy to say, but there must be more to it than a desire for a spring hat!

CHAPTER EIGHTEEN

AGELESS ANEMONES

THERE are animals in the sea named by an imaginative but not too inventive mankind after its land animals—sea cows, sea horses, sea lions and sea hares—and plants in the sea, like sea lettuce, named after land plants. And there are animals in the sea that are just as imaginatively, if mistakenly, named after plants. Most enchanting of these is the anemone, called after the "windflower" of woodland and mountain, an animal that haunts the shaded rockpools where the low tide turns, or hangs in the low grottoes or from the base of wharf piles. You can find them on almost any coast, each with its own kinds— every anemone with its own special perfection of pattern and color, with a beauty as breathtaking as in its flowery namesake and as old as time itself, creatures of water and shade that shun the sun and air.

Touch an anemone and see and feel it close around your finger. Its tentacles pull inside its contracting body and its fluorescent beauty is gone, leaving little more than a soft, slimy mass. Keep one out of water for an hour in the sun and the living symmetry shrinks to a dead leathery scum, for as the water evaporates the lovely form goes with it. Few animals, perhaps only jellyfish, are so vulnerable.

Anemones are soft and readily injured, but to them this

seems to matter very little. Like the broom of the Sorcerer's Apprentice, a damaged anemone is less likely to expire than it is to become two anemones. Of course, this raises a little side-problem of its own. If an anemone is split and each half becomes a whole anemone, who is who?

You would think the soft, unprotected flesh could be easily torn and eaten by the perpetually hungry carnivores of the sea, and that the anemone should by rights be extinct—yet in practice they have an immunity from attack matched only by sponges. It is probably due to their nettle-cells, perhaps to their disagreeable flavor, possibly both. In any case, they are left severely alone by all but certain brave or insensitive large sea slugs.

For several summers I had been collecting anemones from beneath the Marine Service float in Boothbay Harbor, one of the few floats in the region that get left in the water the year round, and can be relied on to yield a good crop of sedentary animals. Where they could, the anemones held tightly to the wood, but many could find no such foothold and fastened on to mussel shells, a security only as long as the life of the mussel. The mussels were packed along the edge of the float and a few large anemones were secure among them. Far under the float the situation changed, for mussels enjoy the light as much as anemones detest it. By lying flat on the float with my arm in water up to the shoulder I could feel beneath. The whole under-surface was a mass of large anemones pressed closely together. It was hard to get them off and impossible to see them. A better swimmer could have dived below to study them—furthermore, the water was cold and murky, with an oil scum on the surface. There is a limit to self-sacrifice in the interests

G

of studying nature, though spectators sometimes seem to doubt the sanity of a naturalist. Generally the observing and collecting of marine life can be carried on remote from the madding crowd, but not always. And like the man who stands stock still in a city street, staring at the top of any building, the naturalist who stands in shallow water and stares fixedly between his feet usually has company in a very short time.

Collecting anemones from this particular busy float was uncomfortably like shaving in the town square, and a prostrate body lying athwart the fuel lines and amid the hurrying feet was a distinct liability to all concerned. The desire to find at least a degree of privacy grew apace and brought with it other questions. Why were anemones so abundant beneath the harbor floats and so hard to find along the shore and in the rockpools? Floats are rarely left in the water through the winter and somewhere there must be an adequate anemone seed stock. Small, first season plumose anemones were common enough beneath the boulders at low tide, but no large ones. Yet this particular anemone is found around the world. Perhaps in our coves the low-tide rocks were too close to the sandy or muddy sea floor. It meant looking farther afield; possibly along the rocky points where the surf beats hard and the water has a cold, offshore temperature the conditions would be so different from the sheltered bays that almost anything might grow there.

Now, collecting animals from a float, that rises and falls accommodatingly with the tide, where you never need get even your feet wet, and collecting from low-tide rocks are two different matters entirely. Tides get lower and lower from half-moon until the moon is either full or new, and on two or three days every fortnight the receding tides expose levels of rock and weed farther down than usual. Not many animals can tolerate even this much exposure to air or sun, and I knew no plumose anemones would adorn the rocky crevices as far up as average low tide. But in the spring and fall the peak tides swing farther in and out, and there was a possibility that the anemones might withstand a little exposure when the air was cool. The early-morning tides would be best, and the stillness of the water after a calm night and the silent beauty of sunrise over the sea always lend them enchantment.

There was the ever-present chance that, no matter how calm the day, a ground-swell from some distant storm would wash the rocks and cancel out that last foot of dropping tide, but I found no swell as I left the shade of the thick spruces on Ocean Point to climb cautiously down the slippery rocks one early morning. Barnacles, mussels and sea wrack gave way to heavy kelp, and starfish and sea urchins abounded in the pools near the water's edge. Occasionally the sea swirled up and flooded the pools, stirring the forest of weeds within. The tide was still on the ebb as I moved along the edge of the rocks, with more of an eye to safety than keeping dry, for the combination of crevices and weed was treacherous as a glacier.

I came at last to a large, flat, mussel-covered ledge that slid out from the base of high, undercut rocks into deep water, partly protected by a natural rocky breakwater farther out. Had there been the slightest swell the sea would have swept the ledge and washed against the steep face of my palisade. As it was, all was still and I was able to lie flat on the ledge a few inches above the water and probe where the rocks and ledge came together.

Weed hung down like a curtain, but pulling it aside I found that the ledge extended several feet in below the high rocks, making a cavern with its ceiling and floor no more than a foot apart. A few inches of water in the shallow basin of the floor made a mirror reflecting the strange, fantastic beauty of the roof. . . .

Here were my anemones, suspended everywhere, with green columns and white with marble veins, pastel pinks and warm browns, and all reaching down to their images in the water below. Smaller than the anemones and scattered amongst them hung slender orange and rose fingers of soft coral, jewels in a many-colored mantle. A tracery of feathery hydroids softened and graced every inch of rock between anemones and coral. It was a hidden scene, not meant for human eyes, gleaming with the eerie fantasy of fairyland. I have seen it once before, in the caves of Cheddar, famous for cheese, where stalactites and stalagmites grow to meet each other through the mirror of water in the low grottoes.

Many of the anemones were as large as they seem ever to get and could have been centuries old. Most animals and plants have their start, grow for awhile, reproduce, and die at their appointed time. A mouse is a doddering old man at the age of two. And if he should starve, he starves like we do. The flesh shrinks but the framework does not, and the bundle of skin and bones finally totters and falls. Anemones are different. They can starve with impunity, even happily, and keeping perfect form and symmetry merely become smaller and smaller. A man I know who kept anemones in home aquaria abandoned them for two or three years while he went off to war. When he returned they were still alive but very tiny, and the sea water had concentrated through evaporation. With food and attention they flourished again.

The size of an anemone, therefore, apparently means little and is more a reflection of its food supply than its age. In fact there are two anemones in the University of Edinburgh that were collected as large, healthy specimens of advanced but un-determined age shortly before 1860. When last heard of they were some eighty years old and still breeding vigorously. There seems to be no reason why anemones should die a nat-ural death in the sea, for there is no evidence that they ever become senile. Yet accidents are all too frequent, and some of the curious things anemones can do can only be regarded as compensations for ever-threatening catastrophe.

One of the plumose anemones before me was already in the throes of propagation of a most unusual kind. Its body was contracted and the marginal part of the base also somewhat pulled in. In doing this it had left behind a ring of small pieces of basal tissue, like a diadem around the parental mass. In the next two weeks each small piece would grow a mouth and a ring of tentacles, and a dozen or more new anemones would surround the old. It is a process called fragmentation and is not infrequent in the life of the two commonest kinds of anemones of the Atlantic coast. It can happen in two ways, by separation of a girdle of fragments without real movement by the parent, or by the anemone's gliding across the rock and leaving small pieces behind.

In either case, we see an exploitation of a primitive prop-erty of anemone tissue, the ability of a piece to reconstitute itself into a new whole. There is an anemone of Japan which can throw off its tentacles and grow a new set, each discarded

tentacle becoming a new anemone. It is as though a man lost
a finger on a buzz-saw and not only grew a new one but
watched the amputated finger become a two-inch person with
the ability to grow large and at last turn out to be a replica of
himself!

The scene was entrancing and even the discomfort of lying
flat on a bed of mussels, with seaweed caressing my neck, did
not prevent time from flying fast. It must have been an hour
since I first discovered this secret universe, and a sharp re-
minder that the tide always turns came with a swirl of cold
water over the ledge that drenched me. I gathered a few of the
anemones and a piece of orange coral to take back to the
aquarium and stood up hastily before a great swish of cold salt
water could complete the bath.

Anemones take well to life in an aquarium and mine were
no exception. After a day or two they became firmly attached
and extended to their full, graceful length. Some remained
fairly stationary on the aquarium rocks, a few managed to
attach to the glass sides and showed more clearly than ever
their animal nature. The flat disc anchoring an anemone to
the ground is able to glide like the foot of a snail, though
more slowly. Small Sagartia anemones can climb out of an
aquarium in half an hour, and even any large plumose anemones move from one spot to another, if only at the rate of an
inch or so an hour. This has its obvious values to the animal,
who can move into a shadier crevice, or away from too much
wave action, but the movement is also an essential element in
the propagative processes.

After several days, when my anemones were fully adjusted
to their new home, one of those on the glass began to glide in

two directions at once, the foot stretching more and more until it began to pull apart in the middle. The gliding apart continued and the split slowly extended up the column of the anemone, until by the end of a week two anemones stood where one had been.

This is a rare though normal process for the plumose anemone, and it results in a pair of anemones able to feed and function from the moment of separation, since healing takes place as rapidly as the splitting. The original mouth and tentacles are merely divided between the two and neither the one nor the other is left without them. A couple of California anemones do much the same thing but with more of the grandiose spirit of the West. One of them, with the impressive and suggestive name of Bunodactis elegantissima, forms extensive colonies over exposed surfaces of rocks along the shore. The colonies are usually covered with gravel or sand, and a tired collector who unwittingly comes to rest on such a ledge gets soaked by an anemone mush. This anemone propagates rapidly by splitting from the base toward the mouth. It happens mainly to those around the margin of a colony, rarely in the center, and experiments show why this is so. Any anemone will split its sides if it is moved to a solitary position where there is room to stretch. If the foot can stretch, it divides; if it cannot stretch, it does not. The ones in the center simply have no room to stretch.

The other western anemone is a species of Sagartia like one of those of the Atlantic coast. When kept in an aquarium it spreads out over the glass as if trying to travel in all directions at once. The central part then pulls back, leaving a ring of strips. Each strip then divides up so that each piece is more or less round, each destined to become a complete anemone. My plumose anemone was similar, though more sluggish. It was almost as though the animal flowed apart like a viscous fluid. As a rule the process requires several hours, but well-fed anemones can repeat it every three or four days.

Perhaps the most enterprising of all anemones is the small Gonactinia prolifera of the waters of the eastern Atlantic, which is rarely more than a quarter of an inch long. It abandons the sea floor for the upper layers of the ocean and swims with its tentacles, wishing it were a jelly-fish after all. It transforms into two anemones in a manner all its own. A ring of new tentacles sprouts from the body about midway between mouth and base. They grow, and then a circular constriction nips the body in two just above the new set. In fact the upper one may start to repeat the process even before the first division is complete, so that you find a string of three individuals still partly held together.

With these tricks of vegetative propagation up their sleeves and no old age looming before them you would hardly expect anemones to indulge in sexual reproduction as well. Yet they do, and some of them have added a versatility of their own. A single individual of Sagartia troglodytes (note its hermit's name) may produce either eggs or sperm or even both at once. It may shed them to drift abandoned in the current, or it may hold fertilized eggs in its interior and liberate them only when they are able to swim and to have at least some control over their own destiny. Meanwhile the young of some others become aggressive adolescents and for a while become carnivorous parasites on a variety of jellyfish.

I never had seen anemones spawning, but a few weeks after

I had brought the plumose anemones back from Ocean Point one of them began to develop an hour-glass waistline. This in itself was not unusual, for anemones aid their respiration with occasional waves of constriction which pass from the base towards the mouth, ejecting stale water and food-remains. This constriction moved up the column and was immediately followed by a second. Then came the surprise. A stream of hundreds of minute white eggs poured out of the mouth and cascaded over the rim between the tentacles into the surrounding water. Wave after wave traveled up the column and thousand upon thousand of eggs were cast out during the next ten minutes.

Each egg was little more than one three-hundredth of an inch across. Each would develop into a tiny hollow ball of cells, acquire a mouth and a long tuft of vibrating hairs to drive it through the water. And eventually they would swim toward the sea floor and settle, those that lived that long.

Among the unseen host of anemones along the coast a few would be spawning each day, and the sea virtually infected with the eggs. Here was the answer to my problem of the float. Night and day, month in and month out, the seed was settling, and whenever a foothold could be gained and kept and food captured, anemones would appear. Most of the seed would be swept away by the currents, or smothered in mud. Some would settle upon some animal shorter-lived than themselves, and have their lives curtailed. But a few, a very few, would find the right place and live perhaps into the following century.

CHAPTER NINETEEN

SCALLOPS AND A DREDGE

It was the morning after a frosty night and the hunter's moon had set. No cloud smudged the crystal blue of the sky and the sun poured with a limpid intensity through the crisp autumnal air. The wind blew out of the north, the hatchery at Boothbay wanted some scallops and I needed some other creatures to take back to the aquarium at McGill University in Montreal, where the sea and its life were almost as remote as the moon.

We put our dredge overboard several miles upstream where the salt Sheepscot River formed narrows and the current flowed fast, and dragged the stony bottom for half an hour. There was no winch aboard, and pulling in a loaded dredge without one is about the most strenuous exercise I know. But if the company is good and hopes of a big haul are high, the work is easy. So we dragged and hauled, here and there, and after two or three hours had the scallops and more besides.

Oysters we swallow whole, clams we chop up for chowder, but when it comes to scallops we take only the big muscle that holds the shells together. I am sure a lot of good food is wasted and I can see no reason why a scallop should not suffer the fate of an oyster. I have seen them swallowed whole and alive with every sign of enjoyment on the face of the swallower. Maybe it is the reddish color of the foot that is disconcerting to the faint-hearted, or perhaps the hundred little blue-green eyes peering out from the mantle edge.

Scallop shells are often strikingly handsome and have been put to many uses. You see them everywhere as symbols advertising an oil company, and in medieval times the same sign was the badge of the pilgrim. But quite apart from its famous shell, the scallop is an unusual bivalve.

Wherever you see eyes you can expect movement, for eyes are never a luxury. An oyster has none, neither can it move. But a scallop, for all its weight and clumsy equipment, can actually swim. And any animal that swims or flies must orientate itself either by light or by gravity.

Scallops have one curved and one flat shell and lie on the bottom with the rounded side downward. This lifts the animal clean off the sea floor, the better to feed and be ready for a quick take-off. Should you see one in an aquarium or even a live one in a dish of water, look at the soft tissues hanging between the shells. Curtains from the top and bottom almost meet, and enclose a water chamber between. Outside the curtains, just within the edge of the shells there is a fringe of small tentacles. If any tiny animal still too large to be eaten by the scallop should bump against them, the shells shut tight. Between the tentacles you can see the eyes, each one a blue-green iridescent jewel, with lens, retina and nerve. And they are present all round the edge of the scallop except where the hinge is. This is the only blind spot.

A bed of scallops may lie still for weeks, like any other bivalves, but let a starfish walk across the bed and there will be a violent scattering in all directions. Muscles contract, water shoots out between the shells, and the jet-propelled scallop shoots backward, hinge first, and gets out of the way. This is the escape movement. The real swimming action is different, for the mollusk literally flaps its shells open and shut in rapid succession. Each time the shells open and water rushes in the animal moves forward with a jerk, almost as though it were taking a bite out of the water. In this sort of movement the water is expelled near the hinge and the direction of movement is the opposite to that of the escape reaction. Hordes of small scallops have been seen swimming near the surface of the sea, migrating to nobody knows where.

Some kinds of scallops are inclined to swim about more than others. I imagine the northern scallop is more sluggish than most, judging from the things that grow on its back, their presence implying comparative inactivity on the part of the scallop that in the end must make swimming very difficult. One that we brought up in the dredge had a sea potato attached to it, and another had a young sea peach like those on some of the stones. In spite of their agricultural names these are as truly animal as the scallop and as highly elaborate in internal structure and activity as any bivalve. The names are descriptive. The sea potato looks like a potato in shape, size and color, except that it has two holes in it and usually, like this one had, a foot-long stalk. Sea peaches are rounder, have no stalk, and have a velvety, creamy orange bloom. Both are sea squirts or tunicates, like the buff, warty sea squirts of the mangrove roots to the south or the jet-black squirts of the Beaufort pilings. All sea squirts have an internal filter-basket of gills through which the water is drawn that enters through one of their two siphons, the filtered water escaping through the other siphon. Yet the internal structure is more like the throat of a fish than it is anything else.

Years ago these animals were mistakenly classed with the mollusks, for the method of feeding and the general inactivity are not unlike those of a clam, and the true nature of the gills was not recognized. But when the larvae hatching from their eggs were examined, zoologists were startled to see not merely a tadpole or fish-shaped organism, but one that has the forerunner of a backbone and a nerve cord that is unmistakably the same as the spinal cord of the backboned animals. Somewhere in the inconceivably distant and murky past our own kind may have had its beginnings in such as these. Sea squirts and man are two ends of the same line.

The dredge picked up a few other creatures, kinds rarely captured by any other means—toad crabs and spider crabs, and large, bright-red hermit crabs housed in the shells of the big whelk, which had their own bizarre attraction. Two stars, one a sun star with a purplish-red center and twenty arms, and the other a basket star, brought recollection of the Tortugas reefs. Each showed the possibilities and limitations of the five-rayed pattern—the one had merely multiplied the spokes of its wheel, and the other had its spokes successively branching, but each was still a walking wheel with a central mouth and no head to direct it.

Except for the crabs, all the animals in the dredge were visitors from the colder North. They came into the salt river only because the bottom was rocky and the water icy cold. A little farther south and you would not find them, but you can dredge sea potatoes and northern basket stars all through the Arctic seas.

CHAPTER TWENTY

ISLANDS IN FOG

SEA BIRDS—gulls and cormorants—live on the outer White Islands off Ocean Point, and they had hatched their eggs some weeks ago. It was almost time for mother gulls to bring their bulky babies inshore to teach them how to forage for food, and for young, overgrown cormorants to fall out of their nests and begin to behave like birds. I wanted pictures of them, and it was high time I went out to get them.

On one of those still mornings that foretold a blistering heat-wave inland, with a belt of fog lying along the horizon that told of cold water and warm air, I set out, in a white Swampscot dory powered by the smallest inboard to be found, and chugged through the quiet, sunny stillness at a sedately civilized five knots. The tide was out, and lobstermen were already pulling traps among the weed-draped reefs in the bay.

Negro Island came close and I took the western passage along the shaded water beneath the cliff. A low swell came in here from the outer sea, the aftermath of some storm beyond sight and already out of time. The water was cool and dark under the cliffs and jellyfish looked blue-white as they drifted by. Then there was a swish and a snort nearby. The surface broke again as three porpoise slid out, along and down in a beautiful curving motion that gave them a second or two to

replace the air in their lungs. They disappeared, and then, a
hundred yards away they cut the surface again, when all I
could see was their black dorsal fin.

Fog began to slip by, and the end of the island was hazy. It
thickened as the island itself faded, and the world became
white and fuzzy, with the sun still bright in the fog and sending gleam after gleam along the water. Suddenly a dark mass
loomed up. I thought for a moment it was Fisherman's Island,
for none other lay ahead, but of course that was much too soon
and the darkness quickly became a large reef. The tide was
low and the rocks were high out of the water, while the fog
gave them the illusion of distance, and so of height as well. It
was a little tricky threading through the lobster buoys.

The fog thickened and I had only the sun over the port bow
to steer by. Land was all around within a mile, but even then
it was surprising how quickly, when everything looked alike
and I couldn't get bearings, an element of adventure had crept
into trying to make a landfall two miles away. As long as I
could see the sun I couldn't be far wrong, if the flood tide
did not set too fast through the passage. After a while a red
channel marker came in sight. So far so good, for this was halfway and I'd made no mistake yet. Then a lobster boat showed
gray and faint through the fog, close enough to talk to but
looking miles away. In these waters you could almost pull
yourself along hand over hand from one lobster buoy to the
next. They are thick, but the only real danger is a rope around
your propeller.

The Rams' lighthouse suddenly came into dim focus, and
another link in the chain was forged. It faded again and I was
alone once more with the fog and the faint ball of the sun,

with the only sound the sput of my exhaust as it gurgled and swore at the water astern. Then all at once the island of the birds lay ahead. The landfall was made and I pulled the boat high on to a weedy ledge. A little of that fog-bound navigation had gone a long way with me, and now I knew something of what the sight of San Salvador must have meant to Christopher Columbus!

I could hear the gulls screaming overhead but the fog was still too thick to see much, though it might disappear with another hour of that hot sun. The water was clean around the island and swirling along the rock ledges. There were rocky grottoes too, and with the tide still low and the birds still lost in the fog it was a good time to see what grew where the surf beat into the dark recesses against low stony ceilings. There was plenty to see, once you got used to the scale of this new world.

Sponges and anemones gave color to the deep walls between the rocks, bright and glistening as the water fell away, lost in spray and swirling weed as the swell surged back. Better than that, feathery hydroids, hanging from the roofs of low, overhanging ledges, formed a soft, downy lining, each like a small cream or rose-colored fern, and indeed closely packed like ferns in a glade. Not plants at all, but animals, some of them had probably given birth to minute jellyfish this same morning, before the tide left them to hang in the spray-filled air.

I peered down to see if any seemed at all unusual, standing knee deep in water with my face close to the surface where the crevice lay exposed only a matter of inches. The swell rose silently but effectively and I found myself looking at it all for a moment under water, the hydroids flushed out and graceful and lovely. The moment passed to an uncomfortable self-consciousness as the salt water stung my eyes, and that was enough of that, though that half-second look still lingers clearly in the mind's eye.

The fog seemed to be lifting as I climbed to the top of the island. It was clear there and only thin bands and streamers lay close to the water. Now I could see the birds, but equally well could they see me, and those that could fly flew. In less than a minute, every gull and cormorant that could get off the ground did so and sailed away, to settle on the water a safe half-mile away. It wasn't as disappointing as it seemed, for there still were birds everywhere, big enough to be ashamed of themselves at their inability to fly or do anything but scramble in haste and without dignity from one perch of insecurity to another.

This was an island of birds and dead trees. Gulls of course do not care for trees, but cormorants do, a hangover from a purely landlubber existence. Cormorants still have a little trouble fishing—salt water gets in among their feathers and doesn't roll off at all like water from a duck's back. So all along the coast you see the silly things perched on rocks, buoys or channel-beacons with wings outspread to dry, trying to assume the haughty pose of the American Eagle. For all that, they're proficient fishermen and go single-mindedly about their business. You never see a grown cormorant, for instance, do anything but fish, rest, or fly home; no distractions, no experimental tasting of crabs or starfish, no detours save those necessary to keep flying over water. No cormorant will walk over grass or fly over woods if it can be avoided. Rule one is travel by air, rule two fly over water in case of a forced landing, for a cormorant on the ground is likely to stay grounded, unless it has a height of land or promontory for an easy downward take-off. When it takes off from water you can see why. The tail splashes the water a dozen and more times before the bird is clear, and fishermen say a cormorant has to wet its tail before it can fly. Even from rocks the flight is downward at first, before the bird gets up enough flying speed to keep it airborne.

Gulls and most other sea birds are light, ride the waves like corks, and are built to rest on water and fly through a gale. Cormorants are designed to do neither. I have never seen a cormorant flying for the enjoyment of flight itself or just to look around. When it is in the air it is flying directly to a spot to fish, to its nest or roost, or to a place to dry off. It swerves only when it has to. Nor have I ever seen one sitting on the water for more than a few seconds, just long enough to change the air in its lungs and air sacs. The reason is of course that the cormorant is not as much a sea bird as it might like to be. Primarily it is a fisherman, which is by no means the same thing as a sailor.

The first sight of a cormorant in the water is sometimes startling, and in this case it is more accurate to say "in" than "on." Its body is heavy and floats so low in the water that little more than the head and long neck can be seen, and without its body it looks more like a serpent than a bird. Watch for a moment and it disappears. Then you do see the body as the head starts to dive and the tail comes up like the stern of a sinking ship taking its final nosedive to the sea floor. Diving generally takes place in fairly shallow water, since a dive rarely lasts more than half-a-minute, and the fish taken are almost entirely bottom dwellers, for the most part sculpin, cunner and gunnel. Only immature birds are inclined to be a nuisance to fishermen by fishing inside the pound nets, a typical adolescent short-cut to an easy living.

Men of various races have exploited these birds. They have been eaten by Indians for a long time, and cormorant remains are the commonest in the old kitchen middens of Lamoine County, Maine. Hunters used to steal out to the rocky islets where they slept to club what they needed. But being wiser in their ways with wild-life than their successors, they took no more than they needed, and would raise a shout to scare the rest of the birds away to safety for the remainder of the night. It is merely enlightened self-interest to scatter a flock and avoid the risk of another fox raiding what you consider your own. Along the New England coast this is a thing of the past, and only along Labrador and the north shore of the Gulf of St. Lawrence are there Indians as well as cormorants. There the birds are still taken, though mainly as meat for sledgedogs and captive fox. The eggs too are collected by the local residents, and outside the sanctuaries the slaughter is heavy.

Perhaps the oldest exploitation is the practice started in Japan in the 6th century, employed in China some 500 years later and continued to the present time. A cord is tied loosely around the neck of a cormorant, loose enough to let it breathe, tight enough to prevent it from swallowing a fish. Thus leashed, the birds are allowed to dive and catch fish, and large numbers are caught in this way by their human owners. Cormorant eggs are taken and hatched under hens and the birds grow up more or less domesticated.

The rocky ledges all over this island were white-encrusted with excrement which took on a glare in the brightening sunlight. Wherever it falls it kills the green cover, scorching and burning where it touches. Yet it is the most potent fertilizer of soils that we know. The great guano deposits of the coastal islands of Peru, one of the richest resources of that country, are nothing more than the accumulation of cormorant excrement through the years, only of a different kind of cormorant and of a number beyond belief.

Off Maine the breeding colonies are mostly on small, isolated treeless islands, and even when there are trees to begin with, sooner or later the guano will kill them, and finally they fall. Then the birds have to build their nests on the cliff shelves. On this island the trees still stand, no longer green but stark, tormented and bewitched by the long black birds that stand like frozen vultures on the branches. Each tree supported as many large nests as it could carry, but already there was a housing shortage, and the greater part of the colony had to build on rocks and ledges at the high edge of the island.

Nests are made quickly enough, in four days if it is a new one, in half the time if it is an old one being made over. The male helps only in bringing building materials, such as rock-weed, kelp, and debris for foundations, sticks, weedstalks and flotsam for the top. Four eggs are laid as a rule, sometimes less, and they hatch after about twenty-five days of incubation. Then comes the time when cormorant parenthood really shows its sterling quality. During the first day after hatching and many days thereafter, the mother regurgitates food into the mouths of the fledglings. Later on when the youngsters are growing rapidly, the mother lowers its head and the offspring sticks its own far down into the gullet, though only when the mother gets good and ready. The more clamor the young ones make, the longer they usually have to wait.

After three or four weeks the youngsters join in flocks and wander afoot around the colony, though they still return to the nest to be fed by regurgitation by the parents. If they belong to those more exclusive families that have nests in the dead trees they keep to the seclusion of their homes until they become literally too big and one by one fall out, too young to fly or to climb back. Eventually they wander down to the rocks and attempt their first flight. Inevitably it lands them in the water, so that they are introduced at once to two new elements—air and water.

Immature and non-breeding birds are generally not tolerated in the breeding colony, and like the Gannets, have to set up bachelor quarters, in this case known as "shag colonies," on some nearby islet.

These birds of the Atlantic coast have had a checkered history. They were abundant as long ago as 1591 and as late as 1880. One writer of 1637 describes a string of feeding birds more than three miles long. But from 1880 to the middle twenties there are no records of breeding birds along the whole of the New England coastline, although migratory birds were seen once in a while. Easy targets, fishermen took them for bait and in 1886 birds with the meat on were fetching $2.00 a piece. At that price it is not surprising their numbers went down.

Twenty years ago, after years of protection, the birds began to come back, and breeding colonies started again at Marblehead and on Old Man Island. By 1944 at least ten thousand breeders flourished along the coast. Finally their numbers were judged excessive and the Fish and Wildlife Service

sought to bring them under control. Since that year, about
100,000 eggs have been sprayed to prevent their hatching,
though the effect upon the population is so far unnoticeable.
If you break an egg, a bird will usually lay another in its place,
and the idea of spraying is to kill the egg without letting the
brooding mother know she is sitting on a dud. By the time
the egg blows up it is supposed to be too late in the season for
replacement, but I suspect the cormorant is more subtle than
we think. In any case, there is a joker of another kind in the
whole business. . . .

Cormorant colonies have their troubles quite apart from
the efforts of men to kill the adults or addle their eggs. They
have breeding associates whose company is not entirely for
their own good. Black-backed gulls, Herring gulls, and Eider
ducks are all inclined to set up housekeeping within the cormorant colonies, possibly because there is safety in numbers
and because the cormorant, with its one-track mind, is a perfect neighborly model for minding one's own business.

Herring gulls are said to be tolerated because they serve as
watchmen for the colony. They are intelligent, alert birds that
rise at the first sign of alarm. But it is closer to the truth to say
that they are tolerated because the brooding cormorant is just
not interested, caring for nothing but her own eggs and offspring and never having heard of communal action. Though
the gulls have an awkward habit of eating the eggs and young
of the cormorants, the fact that they perform involuntary
watchmen's duties probably compensates for it, and even the
gulls' predatory pastime is an ill-wind that still blows some
good. One egg-sprayer reported that out of two hundred cormorant eggs present and sprayed on Bluff Island, all but six

had been removed by gulls by the time the men left, some carrying away entire unbroken eggs in their bills, taking advantage of the deserted nests. With no eggs left, the cormorants promptly lay some more. Gulls in fact are said to raise false alarms, causing the cormorants to take to the air, and then swiftly descending to gorge themselves upon abandoned eggs and babies. It may well be true, for these gulls, for all their soaring beauty, are fast, intelligent birds of prey that eat other birds and almost anything else. They will stand guard along a shore at dusk and take a heavy toll of those sea spirits, the petrels, as they come in at night, with their awkward, erratic flight, to fall an easy prey. By day, the gulls will go quartering back and forth low over the ground to flush small land-birds and pounce upon them.

The gulls lay their own eggs amidst the colony, using any shallow, soft depression, without fear of any bird other than their own kind. They also take care of their young till they are almost fully grown. When the youngsters, often two of them, can fly, the mother brings them from the island to the better feeding grounds of the mainland coves and bays, and it is a common sight in late summer to see the stately white matron stalking ahead of a dark-gray, teetering, keening overgrown baby, showing it where to find a crab or a starfish, and later demonstrating how to break open a mussel by dropping it from a height on to a flat rock.

Where Herring gulls go the Black-backs follow, and the combination is a deadly menace to most other sea bird communities. Efforts to control the rapidly spreading gull population of the New England shore are as justifiable as cormorant control is dubious. When the gulls take over, the petrels and terns depart, which is regrettable, for variety is still and will ever be the spice of life. But only when the Black-backs began to massacre young Eider ducks in Penobscot Bay and Herring gulls raided the blueberry barrens of Maine, was the indignant voice of humanity heard. More than half a million gulls' eggs have been sprayed since control was started and it may be that their numbers can be held in check, and a few of the meek may again inherit a little part of the earth.

In the fall the cormorants of Maine begin to leave the cooling waters of the north, and in pre-migratory exercises fly appropriately in large numbers to Merrymeeting Bay The southward movement reaches its peak in September and October, falls off in November, and all birds, immature and mature, winter between Cape Cod and Florida. You may of course see cormorants far from the sea, in the middle of the continent. These belong to another group of double-crested cormorants, a great band that has its own habits of travel. They breed on the islands in the lakes, among the high plains and prairies at the head of the Mississippi waterway, and follow the river system down to the coast to winter and feed along the shores of the Gulf of Mexico.

CHAPTER TWENTY-ONE

PACIFIC INTERLUDE

WE WERE driving by night along the coastal highway between Santa Barbara and Monterey. The moon was high and the surf could be heard all along, but a damp fog that turned to dreary rain cut out all view of the sea. It was part of a trip to the four corners of the United States. Monterey and Carmel meant Jack London to me and brought back memories of my youth in the west of England, when I was a fan of his. But they also meant Pacific Grove, housing John Steinbeck's "Cannery Row" as well as the Pacific Coast Marine Biological Laboratory of Stanford University, and my wife discovered that a marine biologist, even one on his honeymoon, could not pass one of these places without stopping in.

If you have read "Cannery Row" you'll remember "Doc," the blasphemous biologist to whom the book was dedicated and around whom life in this fish-scented community revolved. "Doc" was E. K. Ricketts and he ran a one-man biological supply house for colleges in California until his death in a railroad-auto accident a few years ago. His book, "Between Pacific Tides," is by far the best guide to marine life on those shores, and when we arrived he was not only very much alive but persuaded us, in spite of the depressing drizzle, to go out before dawn when the tide was low and see life in the tide-pools. It was Jacquelyn's first experience in this phase of her married life.

And so, in the middle of a dark, chilly night, garbed in borrowed oilskins and waders and carrying borrowed flashlights, we cautiously crept down the rocks at Asilomar to probe with icy hands into the cold water of the rockpools.

It was a relief to see a lightening gray seascape gradually emerge from the blackness of pre-dawn and to be able to dispense with our lights. The dawn came slowly with the turning tide and we left the urchins and anemones to fend for themselves. With the dawn came the wind, the fog dispersed, sun shone on the wide sweep of a blue Pacific, and the surf began to crash along the ledges in an ever-mounting crescendo. Looking down from the high rocks into the furious, tormented maelstrom at their base, it seemed impossible that animals and plants could live there, let alone flourish.

Palms may survive the blast of the hurricanes, but not by defiance. The trunks bend before the wind, and the shredded fronds give way to the violence. When water pounds the rocks it falls more slowly than the wind, but it comes with far greater power. Yet the same trick works. The one weed that reaches for the breaking surf is the sea palm. You find it only where the surf is continuous and high. It gives before the force of the breakers, and a row of sea palms will bend over and find the rock. A moment or two later their tough and flexible stalks spring erect, and the palmetto-like blades finger back through the water. Hold-fasts, like clutching hands, grasp the rock beneath.

The animals are harder to see, yet they also survive there. Looking down into the deep pools and the channels between the rocks, in the few seconds between the ebb and inrush of a wave, you can sometimes see the great green anemone, a solitary, surf-loving jewel of the sea that may be thirty inches around. It craves brilliant sunlight as much as any fog-bound land-dweller, yet for a reason entirely different. Its green color is not its own but comes from innumerable green plant cells imbedded in its tissues. The anemone needs the plant cells and they need light and plenty of it. Even if the waves do tear the animal it matters very little, for anemones heal quickly and the result may be two in place of one.

Don't be too engrossed in your search, however. Many people lose their lives each year off the rocky points of Northern and Central California. Every once in awhile an unexpected wave of great size sweeps in from the open ocean and drives cascading up the rocks. If you see one coming and run, that will probably be the beginning of your last great experience on this earth. You cannot run fast enough, and the sea will overtake and claim you for its own. In many places you may still be in danger even if the tide is twenty feet straight below you.

The starfish down on the lower rocks is in no danger, and should a big wave roll in on you, lie down and cling to the rocks as though you were that starfish. The water may pour over you, but it may still leave you on land when it goes.

Look at this starfish, with the mind as well as the eye. It is safe for two reasons. Even without a brain it turns the strength of the aggressor toward its own salvation, as a clever wrestler might, and the very weight of the water itself presses it against the rocks instead of tearing it away. More than that, it takes a 100-pound pull to rip a fair-sized star from a rock. For starfish and their like, as we have seen, possess a hydraulic system unique in the animal kingdom. As long as their mechanism is filled with water, the ends of their tube-feet can be used as suckers for holding fast, or alternately released and reattached for pulling the animals over the rocks.

This star of the surf and rock is called Pisaster and it is there because that is the right place and time for it to get its meals, and not for any idle curiosity concerning the way the other half of the world lives. Pisaster has somehow learned to thrive in the surf and to cling securely to the rocks not from any passion for such an exhilarating life in itself, but from a taste for mussels. Mytilus the Mussel is the real colonist, and no rock appears to be too steep or surf too rough for it to hold its place. Its blue-black shells come together so tightly and so well fitted as to form a knife-edge that can split the face of any wave while it holds to the rocks by a set of byssus ropes as effective as those of any mountain climber.

Like all animals Mytilus is born to eat, and like all but the greatest, to be eaten as well. As long as the tide is in, as long as occasional breakers sweep the ledges, the shells gape a little and the short dark siphons open to the water. Water is drawn within by the unceasing beat of the minute ciliary hairs covering its curtain-like gills, and with the water the oxygen and microscopic organisms it contains. Like most stationary sea animals, this filter-feeder depends for its nourishment primarily on the small single-celled organisms of the sea. One of these organisms, common in the open ocean during summer months, seems to nourish mussels but is a paralytic poison to mussel-eating human beings. We have some company in our sensitivity, for a sand crab which also feeds on the poison plankton, and white mice which get an injection of it, are similarly afflicted. If you must eat mussels, a common enough vice, leave them alone in summer or at least gather them in inlets far from the open coast. One of the earlier Russian explorers of the Alaska coast lost more than a hundred men at one time from eating poisoned mussels, while Captain Vancouver had much sickness on board from the same cause.

Perhaps, if you have a passion for sea food, you may also have crept down to the sea-swept ledges some foggy dawn when the tide is very low, like we did, but with a more specific purpose in mind. Where the kelp is thick at the water's edge, and down into deep water, holding to the rocks with a strength that puts starfish and mussel to shame, lives the abalone. This great sea snail, Haliotis by name, with its famous iridescent mother-of-pearl ear-shell, is even more a vegetarian than Mytilus and spends its life crawling among the sea-forest of algae, stuffing itself continually on sea lettuce and kelp. It clings like a limpet to the undersides of the rock ledges, and its size, taste, and beauty are both an attraction and a danger. Reach for it, try to take it by slipping your fingers under the shell and giving it a sudden pull. You may succeed if you are very quick, but more than likely Haliotis will pull first and you'll be lucky to get off with a severe pinch. There are stories of people held by the fingers in the vise of an abalone until drowned by the incoming tide. Whether they are true or not, why be the one to prove the possibility? Once this mollusk has been alarmed it takes a crowbar to lever it off. The great muscle of a foot clings closely to the rock and has the pull of a high-powered vacuum. Large quantities of slime are secreted by the foot, which undoubtedly aids in perfecting the suction power.

Abalone steaks are said to be delectable when properly prepared and well-enough cooked to be cut with a fork. Otherwise no one can eat them no matter how great his passion for sea food may be. The tough muscle fiber must be broken up before cooking, and the pounding with whatever instrument is used must be good and thorough. Apparently it is worth the effort, for as Jack London says in his "Hymn to the Abalone," "We sit around and gaily pound and bear no acrimony, because our object is a gob of sizzling abalone."

The market for red abalones and for abalone shells has grown steadily, and the demand is such that few can now be found along the rocks any larger than the seven-inch minimum that the law approves. Even in deep water the divers say the stock has fallen off, and a man must walk along the bottom for half an hour to fill his basket. It used to be that he could fill it from a single rock. Certainly this is no fault of Haliotis, for a seven-inch specimen will send out a cloud of about two and one-half million eggs into the water in a season, to drift and develop in the currents and settle where they may. Quoting again from the same doggerel, it seems almost literally true that, "The more we take, the more they make in deep-sea matrimony; race-suicide cannot betide the fertile abalone." But the more we take, the fewer we leave, and insurance against race-suicide is no protection against murder. Even the shells are so coveted that California has prohibited them from being shipped out of the State. The mother-of-pearl within and the iridescent colors without give it unusual beauty, and

the peculiar, elevated openings along the shell, which serve
to discharge the water from the gills, make it a curiosity.

The harbor seal from Maine had long been a friend of mine,
but we had not seen the California seals, and so before we
left we went to Point Lobos. The sea lions were there, seals
if you will, for only the small external ears set them apart—
lively, fun-loving, friendly sea-mammals. It was good to see
them. These are the circus seals and anyone who has seen
them playing ball appreciates their skill and their own enjoyment of the performance. Even when a cue is muffed, they are
bright enough actors to meet the situation. Here at Monterey
they are near the northern end of their range, and only California and Mexico see them. They feed on squid, not fish, and
fishermen should look closer to home if they must find a scape-
goat for a bad day's catch.

The twisted, wind-warped cypresses of Monterey root on
the Point and lean landward in a grim effort to hold their one
place in the universe. The point divides the North Pacific and
is the meeting ground of the sea lion from the Tropics and
the otter from the Arctic whose territory reach south to the
bend of the coast here at Monterey. We strained our eyes hoping against hope to see one, without success, and small wonder
even the hope was there, for as long ago as 1910 a single skin
sold on the open market for $1,700. No animal has been
closer to extinction and yet recovered, even if not completely.
After a century of slaughter and forty years of absolute protection the sea otters are coming back and the earth is richer
for them. If you should see one, you will probably see several,
all with arms crossed on their chests, tails out, webbed toes up,

floating on their backs, cat-napping on the water. Their fur
is the loveliest in the world, God help them, and is slack, as
though they had inherited their big brother's coat. They live
off the coast where the great kelp screens them from the killer
whale, their only enemy beside man, and serves as a breakwater against the sweep of the waves. They may even twist a
frond of surface kelp about them to keep them away from
the rocks while they sleep. Three, times a day the otters take
their meals, morning, noon and evening, and work hard to
get them. They dive silently, without splashing, kicking pow-
erfully with their huge hind paddles, with arms folded over
their chest, to fish on the murky sea floor a hundred feet below.
They take crabs, sea urchins, snails and clams, and somehow
manage to pull the red abalone away from its rocky anchorage.
Certainly they don't use a steel bar to lever it off. Perhaps
they pound the abalone with a stone, for a large piece of shell
is always broken off. The sea otter is nobody's fool—if it comes
up with a clam it brings a flat stone along with it, floats on its
back with the stone on its chest, and smashes down on the
bivalve with both paws. I doubt if an Olympic swimmer
could do as well. If its dinner is a sea urchin, it bites a hole
in the shell, sucks out the soft parts, and licks its fingers to get
the last delectable taste. The world would be bleaker without
this lithe bundle of skill, intelligence and humor.

CHAPTER TWENTY-TWO

SUBMARINE ROCKETS

"THIS is the squidiest year I ever twined in," said the Maine fisherman. Off Bailey's Island north of Casco Bay the mackerel seiners caught sixteen thousand bushel of squid in their nets in one night. That is an awful lot of squid, and though you can sell some squid for bait and some more for college biology classes, there is little use for squid by the ton. They make a squashed deadweight that breaks nets, and they ooze slime and ink and make a nasty mess generally. Only the Chinese make good use of them, drying them for food, or piling them up in large vats to wait for the ink to run from the ink sacs. This they send around the world as the one and only India Ink of ancient and modern times. Within the squid the translucent shell is like an old-fashioned pen; ink and pen together are a good reason for the squid being known as the clerk of the seas.

I have seen squid and squid eggs in aquaria, but never in the sea until this year. We were on our way to watch the Memorial Day Parade and all of us, large and small, all dressed up, took the shortcut across the foot bridge between east side and the town of Boothbay Harbor. The tide was far out, and for a long time now it has been a habit of mine to walk along the edge of rocks, wharves, bridges or boats to look into the water, not

H   195

necessarily with anything marine in mind and as often as not without. Yet mentally focussed or not, anything unusual hits the senses with the same abrupt arrest as a silver dollar on a sidewalk.

It was in this way that I nearly missed the parade, and my family would have been more relieved if I had, considering the outcome. Over the side of the bridge was a broad circular band of whitish stuff lying in a few feet of water, something that had not been there a day or two before. It is not always easy to know when a suspicion first arises or when it becomes a certainty, but while I looked and my family went on, the thought of squid came into consciousness and then I saw the shadowy, fleeting figures in the shallows. Squid they were, darting away and as suddenly stopping, as they chased and caught small crabs. The white circle was a great mass of squid eggs. I finally saw the parade in a pair of muddy hip-boots, holding an old can containing precious eggs, but I was signaled by my loved ones to stay on the other side of the street and let on I didn't know them.

The eggs themselves were enough to show they had been laid within the last day or so, and I went back the next time the tide was low. The great white circle must have been made by dozens of squid, all around the outside of an old tire. Smaller clumps were attached to rocks but none could be reached in a comfortable manner. It was boots again, wading and sinking in smelly, sucking mud, water rising about the knees and seeking out the leak in one of the boot-tops. None of it mattered very much. I imagine most marine biologists were weaned on mud at some time, for it is surprising how natural it can feel to be sliding and slithering and sticking in mud flats. A voice called suddenly from the bridge overhead, "Squid eggs, a'n't they?", less startling than intellectually surprising, for squid eggs are not common anywhere along the coasts. It was the rural postman. This proved that if you walk along the roads and paths day after day, you see things, with the mind as well as the eye, and seeing, begin to think and to know what you see. Anyway, the eggs survived the trip back to the aquarium and rockpool that awaited them, and we watched to see if they would hatch.

Hatch into what? Squid, yes, but who knows what a squid is, let alone what a squid has been or what it might have been? Think for a moment of yourself as a man, a warm-blooded, air-breathing vertebrate organism. No kind of animal has had an origin more remote from our own than the squid and its kind. No animal could be fundamentally more different. And yet no others have paralleled our own qualities so closely, in sight, in feeling, in emotion, in intelligence, and even in motherly care when it comes to the octopus.

The miracle of the squid is not so much the way it shoots through the water like a living arrow as in the fact that squid are mollusks, taking their ancient origin among the sluggish, heavy-shelled, crawling snails of the sea floor, and yet are mollusks that behave in a most unmolluscan manner.

Squid compete with fish on the fish's own level. Of the two, size for size, the squid are by far the faster swimmers, and salvage divers swear they are the more intelligent. At the other extreme of their phylum, or kind, are the equally molluscan oysters, without a head, without power to shift their position a fraction of an inch, forever straining the water that lies within reach for the particles of food it may hold. Both are mollusks, each with a shell, a molluscan heart and gills, muscles and nerves on the molluscan plan, and a system of intake and output of water.

An oyster sits permanently on the spot where it first landed, has no need to see where it is for it's going nowhere, has little concern with shape for it makes little difference, and goes in for thicker and harder shells wherein lies its safety. In the life of its distant relative the squid everything is different. It never rests on the sea floor and has lost the lime in its shell in order to lighten the load. It has the streamlined shape of a rocket, for speed is its specialty. And it has a head with all the equipment needed for oceanic navigation and the hunting of prey.

It can do everything a fish can do, but it does it in its own way with its own unique equipment. It is streamlined for speeding backwards, not forwards like a fish, and is reminiscent of that mythical backwards-flying bird that doesn't care where it's going but would like to see where it's been. It has side fins for stability and planing up or down, like the pectorals of a fish. But where the fish sculls with a driving thrust of muscle and blade against water, the squid draws water quickly in through the wide mantle opening and then sends it like the jet of a rocket out through the funnel. It is truly jet-propulsion, based on hydraulics. Water supplies the fuel-force, the bands of muscles encircling the body and the water chamber within supply the power. And none of it was originally designed for travel, for the whole mechanism is in its basic make-up the respiratory gill system that all mollusks possess. The gills are still there in the squid, lying like feathers in the watery mantle chamber. And because the animal is a high-speed, energy-consuming living rocket, it needs more oxygen than the oyster, not less. So the gills that collect the oxy-gen, the blood that carries it, and the heart that pumps the blood are even more efficient. The fish manages to work with one heart to pump its blood through gills and body. The squid does better, one heart for the body, and one for each gill, so that the gills run on a supercharge. Rocket-shaped, jet-pro-pelled, with special fuel pumps, it's no wonder speed is de-veloped.

Yet what is speed? It has little value by itself, and by itself permits an animal neither to capture nor to escape capture. So we come to that amazing organ, the head of a squid (or an octopus, for they amount to much the same thing). The head is a head-and-hand rolled into one.

Think for a moment about where squid have to operate. Most of the time they prey upon fishes, often far from shore and usually a long way above the floor of the sea. To stay within proper physical bounds it is necessary to know whether their movement is toward the surface or toward the sea bot-tom. So eyes, of a kind, and gravity organs are both necessary and present. Gravity organs are simple, as they are in all ani-mals that have them at all, little more than sacs with weights in them. Squid, like most of the others, have a pair of them, serving not merely as directional organs in the dark, but also as indicators of the animal's own movements. For fast, con-trolled movement has to be sensed as well as governed, which probably is the reason the gravity-balancing sacs of the squid are buried within the squid-brain itself.

Above all, the thing that stands out, actually, figuratively and every other way, is the eye. There are a pair of them, as always in a streamlined swimmer, direction-finders if nothing else. But these eyes are much more than that. I think if you asked any zoologist to select the single most startling feature in the whole animal kingdom, the chances are he would say, not the human eye, which by any account is an organ amazing beyond belief, nor the squid-octopus eye, but the fact that these two eyes, man's and squid's, are alike in almost every detail—that this window out on the universe has been made twice in the course of evolution on this planet, in the race of the iron-blooded and in the race of copper-blooded creatures.

It is called a camera eye and has all the essentials of a good camera and more. Here is the list. I have eyelids. So have some squid. My eye has a transparent cornea to let the light in. So has the squid's. Behind the cornea is an ante-room filled with fluid, in which lies an iris diaphragm, a flat circular muscle with a hole in the middle which is the pupil. Contractions and expansions control the amount of light passing through to the darkened projection chamber that lies behind. The squid eye has all this and so has mine. Just behind the pupil a lens is suspended. It consists of two lenses fitted together, an outer one with a shallow curvature, an inner one with a deep curvature, and the whole slung in a ring of muscle and ligament. The double lens forms the image, the muscle ring changes the shape or position so that the image falls accurately on the screen. All this I have and so has the squid. The screen itself is made of many layers, a light-sensitive layer of cells, connecting nerve cells with long fibers going to the brain, in all, a retina. We both have it, only mine and yours are curiously back to front. And both our vertebrate camera eye and the molluscan camera eye of squid and octopus have dark pigment to keep out unwanted light, and rigid supporting cartilage to keep the shape correct and firm. Other kinds of animals have eyes, admittedly, and they too have grown them by themselves, but their eyes are of a very different sort.

Apart from these organs of sight and balance, and the brain within, the head of the squid is a circle of a few long whip-like tentacles, each with its double row of vacuum-suckers to hold with, and a formidable beak at the center where the mouth lies.

I went down to the pool where I had tied the egg masses to a rock. Most of the eggs had turned white and opaque and were obviously no longer alive. It was almost as though they were hard-boiled, and it was puzzling, for the water was continually freshened by the tide and certainly it was cold enough. A few eggs, embryos by now, seemed about ready to hatch. But even these died before they succeeded, and it was more than time to go back and see what had happened at the bridge.

This time the tide was a little lower, for the full moon had just passed its prime, and I found the eggs without getting a boot full of cold water. The large mass I had first seen was gone, all hatched and on their way towards struggling to grow, but some fresh egg masses had been laid more recently. Two or three reddish-brown squid shot away quickly out of sight, and an old lobsterman in a small skiff pulled over, for your fisherman is as curious as any boy, and asked what I was doing. Any marine naturalist knows well enough to expect almost any question or comment, for as a rule he is caught doing something peculiarly silly in some place every fisherman knows there are no fish. And when you are told "you can't catch fish there" or "shrimp is over there," it seems either rude or imbecilic merely to wave, smile weakly and go right on with what you are doing. You do get hardened to it, as I suppose a painter gets used to a crowd of kibitzers. But the postman had surprised me, and now it had happened again.

"What have you there?"

"Squid eggs."

"This I must see!" And so the old man looked. I was a little surprised he had never seen them before, but after all this really was the squidiest year, and probably I was in more luck finding them than I knew. He looked at the eggs and looked at the water. The tide was dead low and I could just manage to wade to get to the eggs.

"It's fitting, isn't it?"

I asked him what he meant. He looked again at the tide. "The eggs are safer close inshore," he said, "but how do they know enough to lay them where the tide won't leave them high and dry, right at the very edge?" The only answer I could think of was that the squid waited for low tide and somehow knew when it was about to turn, and then laid their eggs as close to shore as possible. It could be true. And he went on— everything in the living world but man seemed to fit, it all made a pattern, though he couldn't see what the pattern meant.

The nearby boulders beneath the surface of the water were festooned with the eggs, with hundreds of cigar-shaped masses of jelly each about the width of a pencil, each small mass containing fifty or sixty developing eggs. I took as many as I thought I needed and put some again in the pool and the rest in the aquarium. At least this time there were eggs at

almost every stage of development and I wouldn't have to wait
for weeks for some of them to hatch. The embryos were held
secure in the fingers of jelly, though each one had its own
small compartment in which to become a squid. Each egg
in fact lay within a small spherical capsule filled with fluid,
and it was these capsules that the jelly actually held together.

Few people have ever seen squid either mating or deposit-
ing their egg masses, and I doubt if there has been anyone
who has seen both activities. It is a rather complicated business, not so much because the sexes are separate and are not
combined in the same individual as in many snails, and only
partly because the eggs must be fertilized before they get all
wrapped up in jelly. These are factors of course, but it is the
combination of these with the free-swimming life of the animals in the open ocean that makes things rather difficult. The
interior of the whole pointed end of a female squid is set aside
for the production and ripening of eggs. The jelly is added
to them as they are passed out of the oviduct into the gill
chamber, just before they are deposited. And to develop they
must be fertilized on the way. That means sperm must be
there in the right place at the right moment. So we come to
the male animal. Squid of both sexes have ten arms, of which
eight are moderately long and correspond to the eight arms
or tentacles of an octopus; and two are much longer and are
used more like hands in the actual capturing of animals for
food, as distinct from holding them. Now, sperm cannot be
shed freely in the water under the circumstances, for it would
do no good. It has to be ready for use in the mantle or gill
chamber of the female when her eggs are ready. So even if the
water carries sperm within the chamber the chances are re-

mote for the sperm to be effective. What happens is this. The microscopic sperm cells are made up into small pencil-shaped packages called spermatophores, each about a half-inch long, in a special gland possessed by the male. As these packages accumulate, the male inserts one of his two long arms down into his own gill chamber, grabs a handful of sperm packets, swims alongside a female and shoves the collection deep into her gill chamber. Then later, perhaps very much later, when the eggs are ready to be laid, each packet explodes inside the female, to liberate a cloud of sperm cells which fertilize the emerging eggs. By this time of course, the independent male may be several hundred miles away chasing a fish or a crab.

The eggs in the pool began to turn opaque and white again, like the first lot. It didn't matter very much for the rest in the aquarium seemed to be healthy enough and doing their best to develop a head and a heart. But it was puzzling, until I remembered something I suppose I had known all along. It wasn't a matter of temperature or oxygen. Embryos lived happily for hours and even for a day or two in little more than a drop of sea water on a glass microscope slide, with a glass cover. If they had been sensitive they would have been either asphyxiated or have had a heat stroke. It wasn't the temperature of the pool water that coagulated the eggs, nor the heat rays of the sun. It was the light of the sky itself, north light if you like. And not the light you see. A simple check showed this, for a sheet of glass placed between the eggs and the surface of the water put a stop to the cooking process.

The difference between the eggs in my pool and the place where I found them was in the amount of water that covered them. Even at low water there was several times as much overlying the spot chosen by the squid than in my pool. And most of the time it was very many times more.

You do not get a sunburn because the sun's rays are warm. Neither do you get it from the white light you see. In fact you can get as good a burn as any in a nice, thick sea fog. The light that burns is invisible, though a bee can see it, and is the ultraviolet light that lies just beyond the blue-end of the spectrum. This is the so-called black light and there is a long and important story behind it, for it has entered into the original creation of life on this planet. It is potent, dangerous light, and living things need to protect themselves from it. On land they guard themselves with pigment, in the sea they stay away from the surface, for the light weakens rapidly as it penetrates the water. What I had done was to bring the eggs too close to the ultraviolet light pouring in from the heavens. Glass stops it, and that was all they needed. Even the intense light from my microscopic lamp did them no harm, in spite of its powerful condenser, for all was glass between and the invisible death rays could not get through.

At first I could see little in the egg. Then after a few days a thick film spread over the egg from one of its ends and slowly formed a sack of tissue around the yolk. And as this went on the first end began to thicken, and gradually I saw an embryo taking form, a minute round body and head. Long before very much of the yolk was used up, the colorless embryonic eyes grew out as striking objects, and the microscopic heart could be seen beating within the body, and the ten tentacles reaching along the sides of the sac of yolk.

Long before the embryo has power to act, the whole egg on which it grows starts to glide and turn slowly about in its

liquid spherical prison, with the seemingly effortless ease of a
dirigible. As a matter of fact you can see the same thing happen early in the development of a frog's egg. In both cases the
outer layer of the developing egg acquires a virtually invisible
coat of fast-beating protoplasmic hairs that cause it to turn
and slide through the liquid surrounding it. The movement
seems to be important in bringing sufficient oxygen to the
surfaces of the embryo.

After a while the embryo begins to grow quickly, and the
yolk is used up just as fast. Then for a time the growing embryo seems to be holding its yolk-sac to its mouth with its
arms for all the world like a baby with a feeding bottle. Finally, after the unborn squid has begun to feel a little cramped
and taken to the habit of holding on to the walls of its capsule
with its fins, and the bottle of yolk is just about disappearing
into its mouth, the prison walls soften and break and the
youngster swims out.

I doubt if there is anything more entrancing and more beautiful than a newly hatched squid. It sounds hard to believe,
but everyone who has seen one has had the same response as I.
It is minute, dartingly active, almost all eyes, but above all it
is covered with innumerable tiny patches of color—red, yellow,
green, black, not in a set pattern but each flashing large and
small, a scintillating jewel of tiny life.

Probably the thing you hear most often about squid, cuttle-
fish and octopus is their use of an inky smoke screen. After all,
why shouldn't submarine jet-propelled rockets equipped with
complex navigating instruments manufacture smoke screens
to cover their escape? Yet there is a danger in this sort of con-

jectural thinking. I remember a visitor at an aquarium who didn't believe in sea horses until he was confronted with one. After that they had no difficulty in convincing him that the "cloth-of-gold" byssus threads of a pen-shell was hair from a mermaid. The texture and color were clearly what you would expect, and anyway a mermaid made as much or as little sense as a sea horse!

Zoologists and others have argued about the so-called smoke screen for a long time. An octopus or a squid shoots it out with the water jet whenever it is seriously disturbed, and there is no doubt that the smoky cloud increases the chances of escaping a pursuer. One theory is that the cloud is really a screen and the animal changes direction behind it. Another is that the pursuer mistakes the dark cloud for the animal itself and the real thing escapes in the confusion. Neither of these interpretations is untrue, but they are not completely satisfying. It is only recently that the rest of the story has come to light. For all its reputation, an octopus is a shy, timid retiring creature, but it has a liking for the same sort of crevices in reefs and rocks as the powerful, aggressive and vicious moray eels, and the eels are the bane of their existence. The moray goes down into the hole of an octopus to make a meal of it (just as gopher snakes go down the burrows after gophers) and the poor octopus hasn't a chance in the world.

The fight is entirely different from that magnificent fantasy of Victor Hugo's in "The Toilers of the Sea." If the octopus is large, the eel seizes one of the tentacles, spins its own body rapidly, and twists it off. If the octopus is lucky, it escapes to regenerate another arm. As a rule the octopus fastens itself to the head of the eel and the fight is on. The eel then throws a loop of its tail around its own body, slips backwards through the loop and forces the octopus off, at the same time gulping the mollusk into its mouth. So when an eel and an octopus were placed together in an aquarium, both naturally became excited. The eel started to search for the octopus, and the octopus went through one color and pattern after another. As soon as the two were a foot apart, the octopus discharged its ink and darted away. Then after awhile came the surprise, for long after the ink cloud had faded away and the octopus was in plain sight again, the eel hunted to no effect, and failed to recognize the octopus even when its nose was actually touching it. The eel's sense of smell had been paralyzed and it did not recover for more than an hour. In other words, what the octopus actually sets off is a stink bomb.

There are obvious differences between an octopus and a squid, but they are much the same kind of animal, and in many ways we know a great deal more about the octopus. The reason is simple enough. A squid in an aquarium is about as cramped as a monkey in a rabbit hutch, and to expect normal behavior or a relaxed disposition in either case is obviously absurd. With an octopus it is different. An octopus doesn't suffer from claustrophobia. If there were such a word I would say it revels in claustrophyllia, for it loves cozy corners, the darker and tighter the better. And since an octopus no longer has any shell inside, it is amazing how narrow a crack one can squeeze through. I once knew a naturalist who had caught a fair-sized octopus, a foot or so long, and took it into a streetcar, safely confined within a wicker basket. Ten minutes later came a scream from the other end of the car, and sure enough the creature had squeezed through a half-inch crack and was sitting on the lap of an hysterical passenger.

Why is it the octopus has such a sinister reputation? Hugo's terrifying description may have something to do with it, but I think he was himself more influenced than influencing. An octopus is never very large and the greatest danger to a man would be if an octopus held the foot of a swimmer and caused him to drown. Perhaps the reason is its huge pair of eyes. Nothing should have eyes that look so much like ours, and at the same time be set in anything like an octopus. But those who have known the octopus well have come to like it, and one of the finest pieces of writing by a naturalist that I have read is the defense of the octopus in Klingel's "Inagua."

Octopi (it is not correct to call them octopussies) do not grow so big, reaching a maximum spread of only seven or eight feet, which means they have arms rarely longer than three to four feet. Squid are another matter. Some are tiny and cute, but others are the only animals that fight the big whales, though they only do it to save themselves from being the whale's dinner. The largest found have measured fifty feet from tail-tip to end of tentacles, and sucker marks found on whales indicate that some may be three times as large. Since they do not have to come up to breathe air and since no gear could possibly capture them, no one sees them, except as manufactured by Cecil B. de Mille in Hollywood, and we get mostly bits and pieces about them from whale stomachs.

The octopus does have a habit, however, which seems rather strange and leaves you feeling there is something just a little improper about it. It concerns the process of feeding, particularly when the menu is lobster or crab. Now, I think we should be very careful not to sit in judgment on the peculiar behavior of animals other than ourselves. We, for example, think nothing of milking a cow, a procedure which might well cause any well-mannered octopus to blush with shame. For an octopus to pull mussels off a rock, open them up and eat them may seem a little unfeeling if you care to put yourself in the position of the brainless bivalve, but it is natural enough. But when a lobster is caught, the octopus bites a hole between the shield and the tail, pours both a poison and a powerful digestive ferment into the body, and digests the lobster within its own shell right down to the tips of the legs. When all is more or less liquid it is sucked into the narrow gullet and the octopus settles down to become a little bigger, though probably no better.

On the other hand a female octopus shows something remarkably like motherly love, at least to the extent of being ready to stand guard over her eggs and tend them carefully as long as she has strength to move. An octopus was kept in an aquarium some time ago at Pacific Grove, a little lady called Mephista. She had a modest shelter of stones in a front corner of the aquarium and a movable board to keep out most of the light. One night in July two or three festoons of eggs were attached to the sloping underside of the retreat, and the same thing happened each night for the rest of the week until there were more than forty clusters. Then she started to brood them. She took up a position so that the egg masses rested against the upper surface of her body, with her eight arms curled backwards to form a protective basket. And all the time the slender ends of the arms were in constant motion, moving among the eggs, stirring them gently and removing any debris that may have fallen on them. She had practically no interest in food. If meat were dropped close to her, she tried to blow it away with water from her funnel, or picked it up with her tentacles and dropped it farther away. On one occasion when the food was returned a second time, she flushed a deep reddish-brown, seized the piece, crawled jerkily out of her little stony nest, straightened all of her tentacles and hurled it away. While I am fully aware that it is reading human emotions into a relative of a snail, I can think only that Mephista was angry and exasperated.

Finally, in mid-September, the embryos hatched, with the same flashing colors of the baby squid. But Mephista seemed not to realize it and went on day after day protecting the empty egg capsules, until one day, after three months of fasting guardianship, she was found dead at her post. Mephista should have had a less satanic name.

Far across the world from the Pacific, in the Mediterranean, is the first and the most famous public aquarium of all. This is the Naples Aquarium, founded for the study of sea life more than seventy years ago and world-renowned both for itself and for what has been discovered there. One of the first questions marine biologists asked when the War rolled up Italy was— has the aquarium been destroyed? The first press report I saw on Naples after the fighting passed it was that the aquarium was intact except for some cracked glass and a loss of sea water, and moreover that the famous octopi were still there.

They are still news, and twice recently, they made the front page of the *Montreal Daily Star*. Probably not the same half-starved, nerve-shocked individuals that came through the War, but youngsters fresh out of the sea. One of these is Oliver. And Oliver has had a lot to say to Professor J. Z. Young of the University of London, for Oliver has an impressionable brain.

The interest of course is less in Oliver's brain for its own theatrical sake, than in the light that an understanding of this molluscan brain may throw upon our own. For the primary problem is what makes us thinking, intelligent individuals, and how has intelligence arisen?

One of the most suggestive ideas is Young's premise that intelligence is a property of a brain that is under continual stimulation, that it is to be found only when sensations stream in from all sides, from touch, taste, and smell, from balance organs maybe, from sound when possible, but above all from eyes. Without stimulus a brain goes to sleep.

Now, in all the animal kingdom intelligence can be clearly recognized only in air-breathing vertebrates and in the octopus crowd. If you have ever seen an octopus lying motionless alongside a sensitive scallop, waiting for the valves to open, and then, when they open, quickly popping a pebble in between them so that they cannot close again, you would have no doubt at all that a mind lies behind those eyes. And when it comes to hunting and stalking crabs, there is no other word for it than intelligence.

So the question comes to this, How do you and I and Oliver absorb knowledge? For awhile Oliver and some of his cronies were kept happy with tasty morsels of sea food and attractive-looking little crabs. Then the finest crabs available were offered on big white plates. Soon Oliver recognized that a white plate meant dinner and came pouring out of his hole arm over arm over arm whenever he saw it.

When he had this association firmly fixed in his head, a

crab was lowered to him on a red plate carrying an electrical charge. Oliver got the crab and got a shock. He drew back startled, thought it over, and tried again. Another shock, and the next day he passed up any crab served on a red plate. Then came a crab on a white plate. He took it, but when he started getting shocks with white plates too, he decided that no crab served on a plate was worth the risk of a nasty shock. So he shunned them all. He could learn and remember!

It was then that Oliver had a little operation. The scientist found the exact part of his brain that stored up impressions. When it was removed, Oliver forgot all his inhibitions and ate everything in sight, shocks or no!

Otherwise Oliver would have started to do what most of his kind do in times of stress—nibble the ends of his tentacles just as though they were finger nails.

CHAPTER TWENTY-THREE

SEALS FOR TEXAS

I HAVE always liked seals. The first seals I ever saw were out of water in a circus, throwing balls from nose to nose with amazing skill and obvious enjoyment. Later on I found them in the zoo of a great city almost as interested in their human spectators as we were in them. A coin in a slot-machine sent a herring shooting through the air to drop into the pool, and the seals on the high ledge dove after it. Seals swim with a lithe sense of satisfaction, and a seal pool in a city park is always the center of attraction, where overheated human beings in envious agony hang over the rail in the high summer heat.

Where we live in Maine a seal comes into the cove regularly during May and June, just behind the herring shoals, perhaps to see who has arrived among the summer people. And a year or so ago the zoos of Dallas, Galveston, St. Louis and Boston sent a call out to the Boothbay Harbor hatchery to send some baby seals by air, so out we went to find some.

The time had to be right, for the state of the tide was important, and we set out at noon. It took us an hour or more to thread out of the harbor past the bell-buoys and channel-beacons, through Fisherman's passage inside the islands, and up the ten miles of salt-water Damariscotta River to the narrows where the ledges cut far across and the tide runs fast.

Suddenly the river turned and widened and the wind was gone. The boat slowed, circled, and cautiously moved close to shore inside the point. Ledges from the point cut the river almost in two here, though most of them were under water with the high tide. The main ledge extended from a green knoll out about 100 feet, with white gulls crowded on its bare rock. A few boulders also stood above water . . . and then one of the boulders began to move. Three or four large seals, almost the color of the brown rock itself, had been basking out of the water and had been alerted by the passing of the boat. As we approached closer they slid into the water and disappeared, and in a few moments the gulls left too, taking to the air in sudden clamor as the panic of a few went through the crowd.

The engineer took the boat back through the narrows and the anchor was dropped a few hundred feet below the seaward ledge. This ledge, like the first, ran straight out from the point, and the two together with the shore line constituted three sides of a box. We cast off in the dory, and the wind blew us rapidly up toward the ledges. The seine net was put over, one end with a weighted rope anchoring it near the tip of the shorter ledge, the other end halfway toward the tip of the long ledge. Half of the fourth side of the box was now closed and the trap was set. Seals might already be within and others could get there, either through the half-open side or through the narrow gap in the middle of the long ledge.

It was a stiff pull to bring the dory back against the wind, which seemed as if it were blowing through a wind tunnel, and the tide had still another hour of flood. But before it could be tied up to wait there was a cry, "There's one in it now!", and a sudden turmoil was visible in the middle of the line of corks holding up the net. The dory dropped back, part of the net with an entangled seal was brought inboard, and the net released. It was a baby not two months old and no sooner was it hauled into the larger boat than a great, brown seal jumped clear over the net, turned about and attacked the net violently.

This was the mother, showing her age by the warm color of her coat, and not so much outraged at what had happened as frenzied by the danger to her other baby which had drifted unwarily toward the net. We rowed back and got this youngster too, though there was no thought of catching the grown seals, especially these mothers. With their intelligence, experience and powerful bodies no such net could catch or keep them.

The first baby aboard was a bull pup and its male disposition was only too obvious. In spite of its recent experience of entanglement and capture the youngster snapped viciously at every foot that came anywhere near. The second pup was female, and gentle from the beginning, although after ten or fifteen minutes that display of masculine emotion had quietened down and it was hard to tell the two apart. They were a brother and sister, which is rare, for the harbor seal commonly has but one offspring a year. I reached down and tickled the soles of their flippers and the male pup curled them up and squirmed every time. His sister again showed more equanimity.

These babies, like all those in the river, were born elsewhere. Earlier in the spring all the seals were offshore, around the outer treeless islands in colonies of a hundred or more. Not only off the coast here, but all the way from southern New England to the Arctic Ocean and to Alaska. In the West the harbor seal extends from Baja California to the Pribilof Islands, only there it is called the hair seal. There is a subtle distinction between hair and fur, a matter of coarseness and curliness that makes it attractive or otherwise to the shorn and shivering human race. Fur is good, hair other than our own is undesirable, and the harbor seal has for the most part escaped from the terrible slaughters inflicted on its cousins. Only the most vigorous and concerted international action has saved the western fur seal, and this for the sake of an industry rather than an innate love of the animal itself. Even some hunters have caught on to the fact that it doesn't pay to kill the goose that lays the golden egg. In the east the Greenland seal winters in all-too-readily accessible herds on the Labrador ice fields, and their numbers have been greatly reduced by sealing for oil. The harbor seal, however, is difficult to find in large, helpless assemblies, its blubber less productive of oil, and its skin of no value, so it is not coveted. The coarse hair varies from almost black with yellow markings to a yellowish gray with dark brown spots. Occasionally albinos appear.

None of this means that the harbor seal is let alone. Seals eat fish, though not exclusively, for clams and crabs are by no means despised. They will eat any fish that is available, with no particular preference for the commercial food fishes, and squid and octopus when present are taken as readily as fish. Stones are often found in the stomach of a seal and sailors have thought it to be for ballast, but it is much more likely that the presence is accidental; possibly it was held by the tentacles of some desperate squid. But whether it be fish, crabs or squid, any animals suspected of eating something man wants become a pest, and in the West this seal is detested by all fishermen. They are trapped, dynamited, harpooned, or shot from power boats, for their insatiable curiosity makes them easy prey. Pups are killed so that the mothers may be the more easily destroyed while looking for them. Along the eastern coast there are perhaps fewer fish, fewer fishermen and fewer seals, but mankind is still a menace to a friendly mammal. Fish have worms and so does everything that eats raw fish. Inshore cod and hake especially have worms, to the violent objection of city folk who find them, baked, boiled or fried. Generally, this sort of worm has to live in two animals to complete its own development, and the harbor seal is suspected as being one of them. So, the world having been made for man, we may yet exterminate the seal and have less need to watch what we eat. Or, of course, we may be quite wrong and merely have no seals.

Harbor seals are no great seafarers and stay close to the coastline, nor do they seem to be able to sleep in the water. They need to come ashore by day or night to rest. For all their rather fish-like form and fancy for fish, they are true warm-blooded hairy mammals of landed ancestry, that suckle their young and bring them forth alive, breathing air and hearing the sounds of the air. True, their feet are fin-like flippers, ideal for swimming and of little use on land, and the body as a whole is streamlined and can writhe with a sinuous motion that is the power-house of their ten-knot drive through the water. But they are born ashore and have to be taught to swim like any other landlubber.

Mating takes place mainly in the fall, among males at least three years old and females two years old, and polygamy is the rule. In the spring the newly-born pup may still be wearing its white, soft woolly fetal coat. It is soon shed and the thirty-pound baby is taken into the water. Swimming comes easy to them, and submersion is made easier by the valves in their nostrils and ears which close automatically as the seal goes under. The pups suckle for the most part on shore, for at first their endurance in the water is very limited. They quickly become stronger and spend more and more time in the sea, until after one or two weeks they are strong enough to accompany the mothers on fairly long trips. Then each mother and pup generally sets off on a private expedition, the bulls having no inclination to follow. Nursing goes on for four to six weeks, but during that time the young have to be taught not merely to swim efficiently but to catch fish in quantities sufficient to sustain them when the supply of milk dries up.

The young seals up the river were weaning. The waters were quiet and safe, as salt as the ocean and full of fish, for the alewives were on their spring spawning run to the fresh-water streams at the head of the tide. Clams were there too, and this was an ideal training ground, with nearby ledges for frequent rests. Every now and then a great seal reared half out of the water to get a better view of the invaders of her privacy and the safety of her pup.

An hour had passed and no other seal had hit the net. Pups occasionally wandered out from behind the rockweed-covered ledges now becoming exposed. Once in a while one came close to the net, but each time the head of the mother

could be seen as she tried to locate it. Then she disappeared
and in a few seconds popped up between her baby and the
net, driving the pup back to safety and a timely punishment.
The waiting began to get a little tedious.

Another pup slipped out behind the rocks and meandered
slowly toward the upper end of the net, but again there was a
driving flurry and it was headed off and turned back to safety.
The waiting suddenly became intolerable and we pulled
anchor and went up river to see what there was to see. Farm
meadows sloped gently to the waters' edge in place of the
abrupt spruce forest and this land-locked arm of the sea
seemed more likely to harbor ducks than seals. But they were
there, several grown seals lying together on one ledge and
perhaps a half dozen or more pups playing in the water nearby,
within a stone's throw of a row of white oaks that fringed the
shore. It looked promising for another day.

As the boat turned back into the narrows our heads craned
as she ran up close to the net—there was a pup so far entangled it looked almost impossible to get it into the dory
without bringing in the whole net with it. It must have been
struggling for some time. The dory was cast off before we
came to anchor and at the same time another pup floundered
into the other end of the net. The meshed-up pup was dragged
in and the net finally released, and the dory pulled quickly
along to the other one. Perhaps it was just nature's way of balancing things, but this pup was caught only by a flipper and
it was vicious. Our hands avoided its snapping mouth, and at
length the flipper slipped out and the young seal sank quickly
and quietly like a stone. Seals can do this almost from birth
and can hold their breath for ten minutes.

Three pups were aboard, out of a requested five, and the waiting started anew. The tide was now at half ebb and the gap in the long ledge was closing as the water level dropped. More of the tidal shore was showing and gravelly beaches were coming to light. Seals were leaving the higher ledges and coming down with the tide, looking for rocks low enough to rest on and yet slip off into watery safety in a second. Those without our purse were still cautious, but two pups drifted through the nearly-closed gap in the ledge. No mothers accompanied them and they had evidently been recently weaned. One passed out into midstream through the half-open side above the net. The other floated toward the inner side and then, in a moment, was in the net and quickly joined the group already caught.

Those already aboard were now completely dried out, and the wet, sleek dark-gray coat they brought out of the water was now fluffed up and beautiful. One which had seemed but a little lighter than the others now appeared in a soft mantle of creamy yellow, setting off its large round, gentle, inquiring eyes. The engineer was sitting on an up-turned tub, which to this lovely lady on deck looked like a perfectly good rock. Before he knew what was happening, she had humped herself over to the corner and firmly but irresistibly edged him off and took his place.

The sun was getting low and long shadows from the western bank put half the river in shade. It looked as though four seals were all we were going to have today, and we should be leaving if we were to get through the outer passage before dark. Then, just as the word was about to be given, a pup came out beyond the ledges and swung inshore. Curiosity was its undoing and the upper marking buoy of the net pulled it off its course and on to the wrong side. It was in, quickly caught, and we had our quota.

The first four pups, like all babies, could stand excitement for only a limited time and were sound asleep. The engine started and a throbbing went through the hull and through the relaxed bellies. It was altogether too much and with wild, startled eyes and rapidly vibrating insides the recently slumbering pups galumphed frantically round the well of the boat. But most kids are adaptable and even this frightening novelty wore off and sleep took over again. Only our last-comer stayed awake and insisted on poking his snout through the water outlet to watch the spray driving by.

The river widened and we came to its wide mouth at dusk. The wind had been blowing all day and a heavy swell rolled in from the open sea. The boat pitched and shipped water, much to the discomfort of the seals who could no longer rest in peace but slithered from one side to the other of the careening wet deck. Rather suddenly we were out of it and passing through the island channels. The red light of Fisherman's loomed up in the gathering dusk and then all at once the lighted buoys of the harbor. Venus was setting and we were back, the seals all asleep again. Tomorrow they would be above the clouds, heading air-express for Texas.

CHAPTER TWENTY-FOUR

SEA HARVEST

We wakened to a gray dawn and could see nothing but the dripping outline of the spruce nearest our cottage. Lobster Cove was thick with a dense sea-fog, the child of warm spring air and icy cold waters. It thinned as the sun rose and its warming rays drove increasingly through to the sea. And as the air quickened and the fog turned into moving streamers, we saw the visitors. A long white boat lay anchored and a seine was strung from one side of the cove to the other.

Herring were running—during the night a carrier from Bass Harbor down east had come into Linekin Bay and pulled a herring net across the cove with her dories. There she lay, white and motionless against a gray and green backdrop. A long, thin line of corks stretched from the rocks below for a half mile to the shore on the other side.

It was early in the morning of the next day that they went into action. The fog was in again, but with the dawn came the sound of oars in thwarts, voices, and the banging of wood against wood. One end of the net was already free and was being pulled into the stern of a dory as the boat came across the cove in a wide curve. The banging came from the other dories as they tried to scare the fish inshore where the seine was still fastened. The other end was brought in, the fish impounded and the long net finally anchored at four corners to make a square. Then the pocket-net was set within and its draw cord pulled. The fish were secure and could not escape even by diving toward the bottom. This was the signal for the carrier to come alongside and tie up, the hatch to come off the tanks, the bags of salt ripped open, and the bailer set going. This was no more than a dip net, though one of enormous size that took a donkey engine and a derrick to operate. Time after time the net was lowered into the pocket, to come up bursting with herring and dripping a shower of salt water. Scoop after scoop of glistening silver fish dropped into the hold, with shovel upon shovel of salt. Within a few hours they would be fifty miles away and in cans. These herring were small and amounted to only six hundred bushels, but they would make good sardines and apparently the catch was worth the trip.

Two or three weeks later the herring really arrived and one morning we found that local seiners had strung half a mile of net from the far shore to a reef and across to a point in the head of the cove. Two large pound nets were set inside and the two squares confined, they said, from twelve to fifteen thousand bushels. Nothing more happened for two or three days while the fish emptied themselves of the red feed. Until this is gone the buyer boats refuse to take them, for the fish spoil in the cans or even before they can get there if the intestine is full of these little red crustaceans on which they feed. But for a week and a half after that the cove was busy. Carrier after carrier came in to dip the herring, coming in the evening and working with floodlights through the calmness of the night most times, to be gone with the rising sun and back to the canneries ahead of the day's work. As the bailer dips and the net draws tight, the water becomes alive with glistening, boiling masses of young fish, unbelievably bright in the morning sunlight. And all around the water scintillates with the scales that fall off and pass through the meshes.

For years men must have watched the myriads of scales floating away before it struck someone that they could be used. Now there is a market for herring scale as well as herring, and the lacquer of the scale is made into pearl essence for artificial pearls. One of the visiting carriers came always accompanied by a scaler, a smaller boat with a curious water-shoot and net. In place of the bailer, a wide flexible pipe was put overboard from the scaler, a pipe with a guard to let herring in and keep hake and other larger fish from entering and plugging the works. When the motor started, a column of water and fish rushed up the pipe into a separator where the water and most of the fish scales took a path to the net hung over the stern of the boat, while the fish traveled a pipe to the tank of the carrier. It was easier work than bailing and the dory men sat back for a change and rested tired muscles while basket after basket of scale and foam was dipped from the net at the end of the scaler pipe.

Where had it all begun? Young herring, full of red feed, swimming in cold waters, is only part of the story, and since the herring is not a fish that limits itself to a small part of the sea floor only, the full story is really a history of the life of the sea as a whole. As we follow the herring we find it is merely a knot in the interweaving web of the ocean. No local fish, herring range from the White Sea through North European seas and the North Atlantic, and down the eastern American coast to Cape Cod. This is all one kind of herring, belonging to a single enormous oceanic community, and possessing tremendous powers of migration. Only the herring of the North Pacific, ranging from Japan to California, seem to be of a different strain.

Let us try to trace the web. In life cycles there is no end nor any true beginning, but at least we can make a start with the beginning of the herring. Herring lay eggs, and large numbers of them, in clumps on the rough sea floor. Each egg is about one twentieth of an inch across and hatches into little more than an animated transparent thread less than half an inch long, barely visible except for a pair of tiny glistening eyes. Attaching eggs to the sea floor, which makes them "demersal" eggs, is an extremely unusual habit for a pelagic fish, that is, for a fish that roams freely the upper layers of the sea. For most such fish lay their eggs in their own drifting world, to take their chance in the sweep and the life of the upper layers of the ocean. Herring gain in two ways. First, the eggs are somewhat safer on the sea floor than elsewhere and a larger percentage hatch into fry than they would under drifting conditions. Second, and of probably greater importance, the developing eggs are held more closely to the nursery grounds where the young can best feed, and are less likely to be carried by currents to regions where survival is even more difficult.

Once they hatch, these minute fish-to-be swim upward toward the surface where their food is more abundant. This is where another strand enters the web, for while the fry still feed upon the remnant of their yolk sacs they fall prey to other members of the community they have entered. Arrow worms, peculiar glass-clear animals of the open sea and really not worms at all, feed on herring larvae voraciously. But by the time the yolk is all gone those baby herring that survive must be catching their own food, and, as they start their own active life, they begin at the lowest rung of the ladder of living things and feed on the microscopic vegetation of the sea.

This vegetation is the sea pasture itself, not plants that you can see individually, but astronomical numbers of single-celled microscopic organisms, some with silicon skeletons, the diatoms, and others without. These are the basis of sea life, as truly as grass on a range supports its cattle. These organisms grow and multiply, using the power of light, the salts of the sea, and their own green chlorophyll, to manufacture proteins, starches, fats and vitamins from the mineral universe. Should they fail to do so, all other living things in the sea would disappear too.

All animals in the sea do not feed on the diatoms directly. It is a question of size. Diatoms are the right size as food for minute animals, and of these last there are two kinds. Some are sea creatures that never do grow large, and the sea abounds with small but mature crustaceans—the copepods and certain small shrimp. Others include the new-born herring, for most fish and other sea forms, however large they eventually grow, start life on a minute scale. Even the tiny copepods themselves hatch from miniature eggs, so small that even the herring egg looks large by comparison. So we find all the dwarf swimmers of the sea and all the newly hatched of almost all the marine

I

animal kingdom feeding directly on the diatom pasturage. The tiny herring, like the adult, has no teeth, and swims through the water with its mouth open, the water streaming into it and out through its gills, the diatoms strained into its throat by the fine grill of the gill rakers.

So the youngest herring get their green, vitamin-rich food directly. When they get a little larger, their gill filters get a little coarser, the diatoms slip through and escape, but the young of the copepods now enter the larger mouth and are held. These, the nauplius larvae of the copepods, feed on the diatoms, so it comes to much the same thing—the young herring still grows. Next, the copepod young slip through the sieve but the copepods themselves now enter the mouth and are strained out of the water. And so this goes on until the herring is pretty well grown, and has become perfect in straining out of the water stream not only the largest copepods but small shrimps as well. Calanus is the name of the most numerous copepod, and the shrimps are euphausids. Both serve to convert the invisible plant life into a form that maintains the life of most of the animals of the sea.

As a rule animals feed on organisms one step lower in order of size, but it always takes a lot of the smaller ones to keep going one of the larger ones. So a small copepod has 120,000 diatoms in its stomach, a herring may have 6,000 copepods, and a humpback whale a ton of herring. Sometimes a large animal cuts out the middleman and leaves the fish alone. The whalebone whales, largest of the whales, plow their enormous bulk through the seas with their mouth open and water straining through the great sieves of whalebone so that the shrimp are filtered out and swallowed. A blue whale may have 300 gallons of shrimps in its stomach. The largest of all sharks, the 40-foot whale shark, does much the same thing, except that the sieve lies along the inner side of its gills and not in baleen plates in the mouth. Even on land the largest animals are those that browse and don't need speed to catch their prey.

It is hard to believe that the microscopic plant cells can be so abundant as to support the fishy world in its entirety. Yet it is estimated that in the Gulf of Maine alone, with its 36,000 square miles of surface, there must be about four million tons of crustacean grazers alone, that is, copepods and shrimps. When it comes to estimating diatoms, the figures get out of hand. Chemically the diatom crop is very much like meadow hay, and in a large area of the Irish Sea it is reckoned to be about ten tons of moist vegetation per acre. Off Cape Cod, investigators in the Oceanographic Institute at Woods Hole have calculated the diatoms to be about 400 million per cubic yard. To get a picture of their teeming multitudes is a little like trying to visualize the speed of light. It cannot be done.

Herring come inshore before they are very large and most of the herring along the Atlantic coast are sardine size. They prowl the nursery waters in search for rich pockets of the forage crustaceans, and generally travel parallel to the shore. When they strike an obstacle they turn out to sea. So half-grown herring are caught not only by throwing a seine across the mouth of some cove, but by a type of trap used for catching many kinds of fish in the new world and the old. Fish weirs have been in use for a long time, usually where the sea is confined and where there is a sweep of inshore current. A long line of stakes and brush wood is set at right angles to the shore line, running as a rule from the high water mark on shore to several hundred feet out to sea, sometimes most of the way across a narrow passage. Herring running along shore strike the barrier and turn out to follow the stakes into the trap set at the end. This is usually a box or horseshoe-shaped barrier of stakes driven into the sea floor, open on each side of the barrier line, but so curved that fish enter readily but get out with difficulty. When herring or other fish are within the trap, the fishermen enter with their dories and line the trap with the seine. And when the tide is high enough for a carrier to come in close, the fish are pulled up in a pocket seine and dipped out.

Large herring are generally taken only well out to sea and the best catches come at the time of the full moon, the lightest when the moon is new. This is deep-sea fishing and is not likely to be a sideline of a coastal farmer. Drift nets are set across the path of the herring and the fish run into them and get entangled unless they are small enough to pass through. These are the herring you find all the way up to Newfoundland and across the cold North Atlantic, wherever the red Calanus feed lives.

Here the web begins to tangle still more, for the cod enters the scheme, and we see to some extent why the great fisheries of the Grand Banks of Newfoundland exist at all. Cod feed on herring, herring feed on Calanus, Calanus feeds on certain diatoms, and these flourish where the water is cool and rich in certain salts. There are some salts in the sea that are in short supply; not the common salts, the chlorides and sulphates of sodium, potassium, calcium and magnesium, in which all sea water is rich, but those salts that the soils of the land are most in need of, the so-called fertilizer salts, the phosphates and nitrates, without which plants cannot live or grow.

The waters of the Atlantic coast down as far as Cape Cod are cold for a good reason. Somewhat in the same way that the warm Gulf Stream water sweeps up the coastline from Florida to swing out at Cape Cod toward Northern Europe, the cold Labrador current welling up in the Arctic and rich in the fertilizer salts flows south along the banks of the Maritime and New England coast, finally to dive beneath the Gulf Stream near the Cape. This Labrador Stream, a deep layer of cold water, is a broad belt five hundred miles wide off Newfoundland where it flows over the Grank Banks, and throughout its mass the copecod Calanus abounds. Naturally the herring are there to feed on it, and since cod apparently prefer herring to any other food, they are there in abundance too, and since man is, in turn, a cod-eating animal, the Banks are fished by Americans, Canadians and Europeans alike. In fact fishermen from Brittany and Normandy sailed the Atlantic to catch cod on the Grand Banks even before Columbus sailed west to look for the Indies.

It is really an understatement to say that cod like herring. They chase them all the way across the Atlantic. Individual cod have been tagged near their spawning grounds close to Iceland, and their journeys traced. Large numbers travel to the Davis Straits and Newfoundland, others as far as the Norwegian Sea and into Russian waters. More herring disappear down the throats of cod than in any other way, but a natural balance is struck and the population of the one fluctuates with the other. Yet both fish work hard to produce eggs enough to maintain their racial existence. And while the herring fastens its eggs to the sea floor, the cod scatters them freely to the currents, and one good-sized cod can spawn four million eggs. The fry hatch in about two weeks but only as fishlings one-sixth of an inch long. Even at that size they have a coarser filter and larger mouth than the newly hatched herring, and as meat eaters from birth they feed at once on the nauplius larvae of the crustaceans. Whereas the baby herring go up to the surface layers, cod go to the bottom for a mixed diet when they are no more than an inch in length.

The herring drifters were still working off shore, out of sight from the cove, and as long as the large herring were there some cod should be still around. The Boothbay Hatchery aquarium wanted some large fish to display for the summer season and it seemed a good day to try and get a few. So we set out, with a pail of herring and clams for bait and half a dozen hand lines. The day was not only good but it was blue—blue sky and blue water and a good fresh wind from the west. In a while we passed the long, low Damariscove island. Only the lighthouse and lookout seemed as though they were living in our time. A few weather-gray houses and an old school house looked no more alive than the two or three bare dead trees, long since abandoned.

We left the island behind and the sheltered bay flattened against the long coastline. A red bell buoy marked a sunken ledge and a cod fisher rolled in the swell as he set his troll line. At last we came to a crab ledge, dropped anchor and let the lines go over. I never have found the thrill in fishing that most people seem to find, and it may be due to a peculiar kind of luck. It didn't desert me now. A handsome red cod was pulled inboard, but I didn't pull it. I caught the first dogfish. And then everyone caught dogfish. It reminded me, with a mixed feeling of disgust and nostalgia, of one night long ago in England. The moon was full, the tide beginning to ebb, and the boat was anchored behind a submerged rock over which our light lines drifted. A high Devon headland loomed black alongside, and over the port side of the boat my father and my uncle hauled one large glistening and beautiful sea bass after another. I was alone on my side and one after another I pulled in conger eels. If you have never had a four-foot, vicious-jawed conger at the bottom of a boat in the dark, with a hook down its throat and a hundred feet of tangled twine wrapped around its thrashing body, you have missed a memorable experience. Fortunately most of the remarks made by the older generation were addressed to the eels. There was no way in which I could have done it on purpose.

So today we caught more dogfish, grew disgusted, pulled anchor and went out to sea for another five miles to the Whistler, a buoy you heard before you saw. Again we anchored. The breeze freshened and the boat picked up a good steady roll, something that has a certain subduing effect on even the best of sailors. The fish tank slopped over, first to port, then to starboard, and more sea water had to be poured in to keep the fish fresh. The water here was deep, and several cod were taken. Then up came a lusk. It fell off the hook and floated alongside, its stomach blown through its mouth by the expansion of the airbladder as the pressure lessened as the fish came up.

More cod came in, and then a haddock. Bait was beginning to run low and I dropped my line over again. I caught a dogfish. Then more dogfish began to strike and unless we wanted dogfish there was no point in staying longer. So we hauled anchor and pointed for the coast. Of course I knew perfectly well that luck, good or bad, had nothing to do with catching dogfish. All it meant was that the dogfish were slow-witted creatures who depend more on smell and less on sight than the cod and so were longer in discovering baited hooks. But the fact that they were there at all meant that for a while little could be caught in these waters except dogfish. They drive the herring before them, and where the herring go the cod go also.

For a time dogfish are a virtual plague to fishermen. No one wants them except the biological supply houses that pickle them by the thousands for biology and premedical students in every college in the land; but while they have a derogatory and exclusive name, they are in reality small sharks, differing from many of their kind mainly in size. Two kinds frequent the Atlantic coast, the Spiny dogfish and the Nurse-hound or smooth dogfish. It was the Spiny dogfish we were catching, as they passed in hordes up the coast. Early in the spring they were mostly south of Cape Cod. They pass the Cape in May, and through the Gulf of Maine at the beginning of June. In mid-June they reach southern Newfoundland, and the south-eastern coast of Labrador by the middle of July. This is as far as they go. Then they turn about and go south again, to reach Cape Cod once more in October and November. About half this six-month period is spent off Newfoundland. Like the cod, they go where the herring is thickest, and it is not too clear to what extent they follow the herring or drive the herring.

If you ever catch a dogfish or get close enough to a large shark, look closely at its head. These fish have been in the sea much longer than the bony-finned fish and are much less specialized. There is an opening behind each eye that opens and closes regularly, opening as water is drawn through it into the throat, closing when it is forced from the throat out through the open gill slits. It is really the first gill slit re-employed to take water in instead of passing it out, so as to free the mouth for feeding exclusively. Its particular interest is that we too retain this first gill slit as the passage from our outer ear into the back of our throat. The eardrum closes it, to be sure, but break the thin drum membrane and you can draw water through your ears into your throat almost as well as a dogfish.

The fish in our tank looked as though they had had about as much close confinement as they could stand, and a fast stream of sea water was pumped in through a hose which seemed to help a little. Spray began to come over the top of the wheelhouse and the sea turned dark and forbidding. Thunderheads were gathering over the land and it was better to be behind Damariscove before the storm broke. The cod troller was also driving hard for shelter and our two boats kept pace for a mile or so. We made it as cold air coming from north of the Great Lakes hit the sea and blew whitecaps across the inky black water. At last we reached the dock and hauled the fish ashore. It surprised me to see how fast they recovered in the large aquarium tanks. All did but a few dogfish, and these we opened up to see if they had young inside. Three of them were mature females, and of these one had a young "candle" and the other two several lively embryos attached by a stalk to large yolk sacs.

Cod and herring, for all their different egg-laying habits, are typical of most marine animals in producing astronomical numbers of comparatively small eggs that are left to fare as best they can. There is an alternative to this, which we find in dogfish and other sharks, and in man and other mammals.

The important thing is not how many eggs start to develop, but how many complete their development and growth to reach reproductive maturity. In a way, it is much more wasteful of cod stuff for each cod to cast four million eggs adrift every season in order for one or two to grow up, than it is for a dogfish to produce a few enormous eggs every other year of which one will probably live to reproduce in its turn. Yet both methods are effective. The Spiny dogfish retains its enormous eggs within its oviducts, as a pair of "candles" each containing from one to four eggs, and taking nearly two years to develop. The cycle is very regular and well-adjusted to the annual migration up the coast. Eggs the size of hens' eggs are fertilized within the body of the mother during the time the dogfish winter in the not-too-cold waters south of Cape Cod. By the time they reach Maine early in June, each egg in a candle has a small embryo attached by a stalk to the large mass of yolk. Such was the degree of development of the candles in the fish I had opened. The others had perfectly formed young dogfish about five inches long, also attached by stalks to a decidedly smaller sac of yolk. These were one year older. A year ago they were no more advanced than the first, but they had already made the trip north and to the south again within the mother, and now were going north for the second time. When they returned in the fall they would have used up almost all of the yolk, and by the time the parents reached their winter quarters, their offspring, two to eight according to the size of the mother, would be born. And they would not be helpless young liable to be eaten at once, but small sharks as much as a foot long.

So as the days begin to lengthen, in every other year, baby dogfish are born to each mature female and a new batch conceived, to be incubated for two long years. In the case of the Spiny dogfish, all the food for development comes from the enormous mass of yolk in the egg, and all the embryo gets directly from the mother is protection and oxygen. The smooth dogfish goes much further and has arrived at a state very much like that of the warm-blooded mammals. The egg yolk is used up fairly rapidly, and for the last two-thirds at least of the period of pregnancy, the young obtain their essential supplies through a complex system of blood vessels that intermingle, though do not actually fuse, with those of the parent. In both cases however live births are accomplished.

The summer drew on and herring, dogfish and cod all disappeared and there was little or no fish at the market. Even on the rocky coast of Maine, the water became warm enough for comfortable bathing. Then one day a strange ship appeared, a stranger in Maine waters at least, a pogy boat from Virginia with a high crow's-nest. A pogy boat would come north only if the pogies themselves were coming north, and what made it news was that the pogy, or menhaden, had been a golden bonanza to Maine factories up to sixty years ago, and hope springs eternal in the Mainiac as well as other human breasts. No Virginian is allowed to catch a Maine fish, so a native-born crew soon took over. There is even some doubt whether a fish in Maine waters is the same as any other fish—it was recently proposed that the American lobster, Homarus americanus, should be formally known as Homarus mainensis as long as it lives within the territorial waters of the State of Maine.

Only a few of the local fishermen were ready for the pogies, for gear which is designed for mackerel or herring is too light for hauling catches of the large four-pound menhaden. But a boat from Bailey's Island followed a school right into the cove where the herring had been a month before.

There was a little more action this time, for it was no longer just a matter of running a seine across the cove after the fish were inside, but of spotting a school and circling fast around it with the net flying off the dory stern to form a closed trap at once. Nor was there any point in keeping the golden fish waiting before dipping them out into the boat. In the first place no one was going to eat them, canned or otherwise, for menhaden are processed for oil and fish meal. Also they do not have "red feed" for they do not feed on animal life at all, so far as they can help. These are fish that feed all their lives like the newly hatched herring. The difference is that the straining sieve attached to their gill arches is finer than the herrings' and holds back the diatoms to eat. Menhaden are as truly vegetation grazers as Calanus itself.

A rich diatom crop by itself would not draw the menhaden up the coast from southern waters. What really brought them was the same thing that caused the herring to disappear sooner than usual. Herring and Menhaden like water of different temperatures. When the sea temperature rises much above 50° F., herring move on to colder regions. Menhaden are warm water fish that die at temperatures below 50° F., and like it to be between 60 and 70° F. What actually had been happening was an unusual influx of warm southern water along the coast of Maine, bringing the pogies with it and bringing about a strategic withdrawal on the part of the herring.

This is the way the web is woven, though these are but a few of the strands. Along the edge of the sea, where the tide ebbs, the web has a transient fishy fringe, though the fish that live there are mainly concerned with holding their place and feeding without wandering too far from home. Since the last thing they want to do is to go chasing over the high seas, they have no use for beautiful, streamlined bodies. Some of these inshore, rock-loving fish are, as a result, among the ugliest of all living creatures and could easily take their place among the gargoyles of the Notre Dame. If you have ever seen a sculpin or a sea raven, you will know what I mean. Yet in their own way their shape and character are as fitting as the sweeping curves of a porpoise. They have a tail merely to move them from one sheltered spot to another close by, a stomach of a good capacity to hold some of the large meals these fish can capture and a mouth that stretches from ear to ear and seemingly half way back to the tail. Their skin and fins are so mottled and fringed that they look like a weed-covered stone, and they stay motionless, waiting for some unlucky fish, shrimp or crab to wander too close. Then a huge mouth gapes suddenly, the careless one is swept within with the rush of water, and the jaws snap shut. Through it all the raven or sculpin has not moved except to open and shut its mouth. The greatest danger they themselves run comes from above. One of the most amazing spectacles I have ever seen, and one that always brings a lump to my throat, was early one morning when the tide was extremely low and the gray fog just beginning to lift off the draped weeds and still water of our cove. A great blue heron stood poised at the end of the farthest ledge, with its head back and its long beak held like a javelin. Then came a lightning thrust and for a moment or two a large sculpin was held transfixed across the beak while the heron manipulated it till it could be swallowed head first, the only way a whole fish can be swallowed. Then for about twenty minutes the heron stood there gulping, and with each gulp the huge bulge in its long neck descended another inch. Only when it was all the way down did the bird decide that enough was enough and flew away to digest matters.

There is another fish that you rarely see, though it is often taken on the hook, which lives and looks not unlike the sculpin, though in deeper water and on a somewhat larger scale. This is the northern angler or monk fish. Three feet long, with a mouth a foot-and-a-half wide, it lies on the sea floor and actually dangles a filament of its dorsal fin in front of its closed mouth, the end of the filament spread out like a small fish. Sure enough, smaller fish come to the angler's bait and fall into the trap when the mouth opens and the water rushes in. It is a slimy, ugly brute with none of the appeal of its relatives in the Sargassum weed, the colorful little fishing frogs. I have seen it but seldom, though its spawn lay across our rocks one day, stranded by the ebbing tide, a foot-wide sheet of jelly twenty to thirty feet long, enough to fill a large pail, with countless thousands of developing angler eggs imbedded within. In itself this is a form of protection, for while most fish could strain and swallow angler fish eggs and embryos, I doubt if any could handle the gelatinous mass as a whole. It is much too bulky and too slippery, and even to get it into a pail was difficult because it would slither out over one side as fast as I could pour it in over the other.

Perhaps we can tie a knot in this shore-line fringe with the lumpsucker. The ten-pound adults prefer the rocks and weeds of deepish water, but almost every time I have searched a float or a mooring for some marine growths I have inadvertently caught one or two young green lumpsuckers, beautiful little fish that had been holding tightly to the wood. When you look at their pelvic fins, once used only in swimming, you see they have become transformed into a sucker that can hold the fish to a rock or a plank so firmly that few waves can dislodge it.

CHAPTER TWENTY-FIVE

THE SEA IN THE CITY

FROM fall until spring we live in Montreal, and nothing could seem more remote from the sea and all its works than a large inland city, though with the coming of a late spring thaw the ocean-going boats creep up the river into port from the Gulf more than half-a-thousand miles away. I detest all cities, but Montreal has its points, not the least being Mount Royal itself. In fact a city embraced by a great river, with a 700-foot volcanic cone rising from its heart, has every natural advantage to start with. From the mountain top you look down across the river, and in between the city spreads out on three levels, commerce and shipping at the river level, hotel and shopping districts on a broad, flat plateau two hundred feet higher, and a residential plateau fifty feet higher still girdling the mountain like the first. For a city on this continent it is already old, and a few hundred yards along the upper terrace from where we live there is a sign that marks the site of the even more ancient Indian town of Hochelaga.

Yet the sea has been here, and more than once.

Ours is a downtown district and since grass is hard to grow, we laid flagstones in our backyard, flat slabs of limestone we found exposed in woods not far away. Each piece was thickly studded with shells and other fragments that had been animal

structure at one time. This limestone was not merely fossilifer-
ous; in places it seemed to be practically all fossils.

This was the first time we heard the sea above the roar of
city traffic. The limestone was Ordovician, the oldest but one
of all the great rock periods that left fossils, and its story starts
and ends a long time ago. If you could go back into the past
about five hundred million years you would find no Mount
Royal and no St. Lawrence River Valley, only a salt sea. Any
land that lay above the water was as desolate a desert as any
now on earth, with nothing green or nothing moving but dust
blown by the wind. The living world lay entirely beneath the
waters, a world without land plants or land animals, a sea
of invertebrate animals where no backboned fish challenged
the sway of the mollusks and crustaceans.

This was the world we put into our backyard in the form of
consolidated slabs. The limestone was the ancient muddy ooze
of that old sea floor, littered and filled with the shells of the
dead or dying animals that lived hereabouts. Some of the remains are so thickly numerous that the animals must have
lived quite happily on the surface of the mud itself. For in
this region at least, nine-tenths of all the fossils are either lamp
shells or sea mats. (Completely soft-bodied animals like the
jellyfish or tubeless worms, with no hard parts and almost all
water themselves, could leave no trace when they died, though
they may well have been abundant; the hard calcareous shells
and skeletons of the others have become further mineralized
within the hardened mud to become true fossils.)

Lamp shells look like bivalve mollusks, but actually they
constitute a group of their own, for their internal structure is
unique and there is nothing really like them. They still flour-

ish in cold and rather deep water, and even close inshore along the northeastern Atlantic coast. You can tell them from mollusks by the way the end of one shell curves round the other at the hinge like a lamp of biblical times. Sea mats, colonial calcareous animals, still grow everywhere on the rocks and the weeds.

Such was the bottom fauna, a carpet of lamp shells alternating with a miniature forest of sea mats. A few miles farther west, where the sea may have been a little shallower, hordes of marine snails lived everywhere, but whether they fed upon ancient seaweeds or were meat-eaters that fed upon lamp shells, we do not know.

Here and there lived five-rayed echinoderms, a variety of them with some modern kinds missing and some now-extinct kinds among the commonest. Stalked sea lilies grew and the broken stalks are fairly common in the limestone, and other stalked members of the "sign of five" lived among them. Here, in fact, is the clue to the limitations of starfishes and sea urchins. Their ancestors were stalked animals, and their characteristic five-rayed pattern is associated with that kind of life. When at last they managed to dispense with the stalk, it was far too late to change the basic pattern, and forever after no starfish or urchin has been able to make up its so-called mind which end goes first for more than a few minutes at a time.

In places the limestone also held cup coral and reef corals, as true a coral as any now living in the Dry Tortugas where our tale began. Probably that means these old seas of high latitudes were much warmer than they are now.

Rarest of all, here and there in the limestone, you find the fossil shell of a mollusk somewhat like an octopus, with the

same great eyes and long tentacles, but one that had to lug
around a straight, pointed shell up to twelve or fifteen feet
long. And with them, their armor just as well preserved, are
trilobites, crustaceans about the size of crabs but of a kind
that no longer exist.

All this was so very long ago it is difficult to get any sort
of sense of the immensity of time that has elapsed. Even the
period of a hundred million years that this region lay beneath
the sea is beyond real comprehension, and still it was only
after this that the land rose, the shallow ocean drained away,
the layers of sea-laid mud and rock tilted, and volcanoes
spouted into the air. One of these, which used to be a mile
high, has left its stump as our present municipal mountain.
Time and more time wore the volcanoes down till only their
roots are left, and little happened in this part of the world,
as far as anyone knows, until the great ice caps of the recent
ice age descended over North America. This was long ago
enough, but when you stop speaking in terms of hundreds of
millions of years, or even a million years, and come down to
a matter of a few tens of thousands, we are more or less in
modern times. At least we reach a time which includes human
history, even if it is an unwritten history, and it is quite likely
that just south of the ice cap the basket weavers were already
at work on this continent.

Ice covered this valley with a mile-thick cap like that of
Greenland today. When it melted, the level of the sea rose
slowly as the ice became water. And finally the land itself rose
as the weight of the ice was lifted from its back. Only it rose
more slowly than the water, and for awhile, the sea flooded
in again over the valley, a cold, icy, arctic sea that washed and

surged along the shore and islands of the valley. The sea floor became mud again, and in the mud accumulated myriads of small empty shells of Foraminifera. There is no other name for them. They are the calcareous shells of single-celled animals that abound in cold seas, large enough to be seen by the naked eye. And the clay which is being dug to make way for a new building on our campus a little way down the street is mixed through and through with these tiny shells. They are not fossils, for they have not undergone any mineral change. They are simply the shells cast up or left behind by the sea that beat against the slope of the mountain. They are old perhaps, but no older than the Arctic Mammoth, and frozen mammoth meat has actually been eaten not too long ago by a few rashly adventurous human beings.

So almost at the beginning and the end of time has the sea swept where these streets now are. The upper plateau was a wide beach where the surf pounded and the sea ebbed and flowed. As the land rose again, the sea beat against a lower beach—now our larger plateau of hotels and shops. And again with the rising of the land the sea fell back once more and washed against the base of the mountain.

Now the sea is a few feet lower still, and all that reaches the city is a one-inch rise and fall of river water, as the distant, living tide pulsates far down the Gulf.

INDEX

INDEX

abalone, 191, 192, 194
Africa, 23
Agassiz, Alexander, 40
Agassiz, Louis, 40, 142
age, 166
Alaska, 191, 217
Alpheus, 59
Alps, 74
American Museum of Natural History, 80, 81
anemone, 162
  dahlia, 147
  great green, 189
  plumose, 164, 167, 170
  sargartia, 168, 169
  snake-lock, 144
angler fish, 5, 240
angler spawn, 241
Aquaria, public, 143
aquarium, 168
Arcachon, 89
Arctic Ocean, 217
Ash, Thomas, 80
Asilomar, 188
Atlantic Ocean, 73
Atlantic Palolo, 30
Australian Barrier Reef, 10, 26
Azores, 22

Bahamas, 4, 62, 117
Bailey's Island, 195, 238
Baja California, 217
Band Snail, 103
barnacle, 133, 135
  breeding, 136
barracuda, 37, 47, 48, 49
basket star, 175
Bass Harbor, 223
Bavaria, 74
Beaufort Island Bridge, 66
Beaufort, N. C., 60, 65, 81
Beebe, William, 14
Bering Straits, 75
"Between Pacific Tides," 187
Bigelow, Robert Payne, 37
Bird Key, 20, 21, 63
Black Sea, 74
blue crab, 84, 85, 93
Boothbay Harbor, 108, 163, 195, 214
Boothbay Hatchery, 232
boring gland, 100
Boston, 142, 214
Botryllus, 150
Brazil, 80
brittle star, 145
Bumpus, 17

Bunodactis elegantissima, 169
Bush Key, 19, 20, 21
butterfly fish, 50
"byssus," 68

Calanus, 228, 230, 231, 238
California, 67, 120, 169, 189, 192, 193, 226
Caligula, Emperor, 18
Cambrian, 26
camera eye, 200
Canada, 46
Canadian Government, 119
cancer, 46
"Cannery Row," 187
Cape Cod, 55, 65, 80, 97, 105, 186, 226, 229, 231, 234
Cape Hatteras, 65
Carboniferous period, 78
cardinal fish, 52
Carnegie Marine Laboratory, 1, 6, 33, 54
Casco Bay, 105, 195
Cassiopeia, medusa, 37, 38
casuarina, 6
catfish, 77
    earstones, 78
    eggs, 81, 82
    male incubator, 83
    voice, 79
    whiskers, 81
    young, 83
Central America, 75
Cheddar, 166
Chesapeake Bay, 85, 88, 93
China, 181
chiton, 126
chordates, 1

clam, 86, 97, 119
    long-neck, 100
    surf, 102
Clark, Leonard, 33
cloth-of-gold, 68
coat-of-mail shell, 126
coconut, 2
coconut crab, 56
cod, 230, 231, 234, 236
    eggs, 232
    migrations, 231
Columbus, Christopher, 17, 22, 178
comb jelly, 157
conch, 52, 103
conger eel, 233
copepod, 228
coral, 25, 28, 244
coral fish, 49, 50
cormorant, 176
    diving, 180
    feeding young, 182
    wings, 179
Cornwall, 18
Coste, Professor, 89
crab, 126
    blue, 85
    coconut, 56
    fiddler, 57
    ghost, 57
    gills, 56
    hermit, 56, 160, 175
    land, 57
    pistol, 59
    speed, 55
    spider, 175
    toad, 175
Cuba, 4, 17, 36
cuttlefish, 119

Dallas, 214
Damariscotta River, 214
Damariscove, 235
Darwin, Charles, 140
Davis, John, 23
Davis Straits, 231
Delaware River, 73
Deraniyagala, 11, 13
Devon, 139, 144, 233
Devonian period, 78
Diadem, 26
diatoms, 227, 228
dogfish, 233, 234
    candles, 236
    pregnancy, 237
dogwhelk, 136, 137
Dohrn, 3, 5, 6
Dohrn, Anton, 3
Dohrn, Richard, 3
dollars, sand, 159
Dorset, 142
Drake, Sir Francis, 151
dredging, 172
drill, oyster, 91
Dry Tortugas, 1, 8, 18, 60

earthworm, 6
East Indies, 11, 75
Echinoderms, 146
Edinburgh University, 167
eel, 207
    grass, 5, 117, 119
egg collar, 107
egg spraying, 184
Eider duck, 184
English Channel, 118, 139, 142
euphausids, 228
Europe, 74, 75

Everglades, 36
eye of squid and man, 200

fiddler crab, 57, 58, 59
Fish and Wildlife Service, 183
Fisherman's Island, 177
fishing frog, 5, 240
flat fish, 159
flatworm, 5
Florida, 62, 102, 116, 231
flounder, 158
Foranimifera, 246
Fort Jefferson, 6, 35, 44
France, oyster farming, 85
frigate bird, 10, 19
frog, cancer in, 46

Gaff-Topsail Catfish, 79
Galileo, 31
Galveston, 214
Gannets, 183
ghost crab, 57, 58
giant clam, 39
Golden Hind, 151
Gonactinia prolifera, 170
Gorgonocephalus, 27
Gosse, Philip, 142
Grand Banks of Newfoundland, 4,
    231
gravity organs, 199
Great Barrier Reef, 26
Greenland, 217, 245
Green Turtle, 9, 14, 15, 16
gribble, 154, 155
guano, 20, 182
Gudger, Eugene, 80, 83
Gulf of Maine, 2, 72, 229, 234
Gulf of Mexico, 2, 18, 72, 75, 186

Gulf Stream, 2, 4, 18
gull, Black-backed, 184, 185
  Herring, 184, 185

haddock, 234
halibut, 159
Haliotis, 191, 192
Hampton Roads, 95
Hatteras Light, 66
Hawksbill turtle, 9, 15
Head Cove, 159
hermit crab, 56, 98, 160
heron, 240
Heron Island, 10
herring, 223
  eggs, 226, 232
  weir, 230
Hess, Walter, 33
Himalayas, 74
Hochelaga, 242
Holland dykes, 153
Homarus americanus, 238
Hooker, Davenport, 8
horse-mussel, 132
horseshoe crab (see Limulus)
Hugo, Victor, 207
hydroids, 66, 147, 150, 155, 160,
  166, 178

Iceland, 231
ice age, 245
"Inagua," 209
India, 74
India Ink, 195
Indian Ocean, 73
Indo-China, 75
Irish Moss, 121, 124, 125
Isthmus of Panama, 75

Jamaica, 37, 142
Japan, 30, 181, 226
jellyfish, 37, 66
  constitution, 40
  locomotion, 41
  regeneration, 43
  reproduction, 44
Jurassic period, 74

kelp, 120
keyhole dollar, 67
Key West, 3, 46, 54
kitchen midden, 181
Klingel, G. C., 209

Labrador, 181, 217
Labrador Stream, 231
lamp shells, 243
Leatherback turtle, 9, 15
limpet, 126
Limulus, blood, 72
  breeding, 72
  distribution, 73
  habits, 69
  history, 74, 75, 76
  locomotion, 70
  molts, 72
  respiration, 71
Lincoln, 36
Linekin Bay, 157
lobster, 108-115
  balancing organ, 112
  breeding, 114
  -canning, 109
  Norway, 110
Lobster Cove, 108, 157, 223

Loggerhead Key, 1, 6, 7, 8, 12, 20, 21, 23, 24, 40, 45, 49, 65
Loggerhead Light, 7
Loggerhead sponge, 144
    turtle, 9, 12, 15
London, Jack, 187, 192
London Zoo, 18
Long Island Sound, 5, 72, 85
Long Key, 30, 46
lumpsucker, 241
lusk, 233

Magellan, Strait of, 120
Maine, 2, 67
mammoth, 246
manatee grass, 22
mangrove, 2, 20, 22
    migrations, 23
Man-o'-War Bird, 19
Marblehead, 183
Marcgrave, George, 80
Marquesas, 3, 5, 23, 52
Martha's Vineyard, 5
Maryland, 75, 76, 95
Massachusetts, 105, 108
Mast, S. O., 8, 12
Mauritius, 16
Mayer, Alfred Goldsborough, 31, 40
McGill University, 172
Mediterranean, 17, 62, 68, 74, 118
medusa, 37, 38, 39
megalops, 93, 94
melangena, 102, 103
menhaden, 237, 238
Mephista, 210, 211
Merrymeeting Bay, 186
Mexico, 67, 193

Miami, 1
Mille, Cecil B. de, 209
Mississippi, 4, 186
Mock Turtle, 11
monk fish, 240
Monterey, 187, 193
Montreal, 242
Montreal Daily Star, 211
moon snail, 98
    boring mechanism, 100
    spawn, 106
moray eel, 51, 207
Mount Royal, 242
Mudd, Dr., 36
mussel, 86, 130, 145, 190
Mytilus, 190

Naples, 211
Naples Aquarium, 3, 211
nauplius larva, 134, 228
needle-like fish, 52
Negro Island, 176
Negroes, West Indian, 49
New England, 46, 104, 181, 185, 217
Newfoundland, 142, 230, 234
Newport River, N. C., 82
noddy tern, 20
North Carolina, 60, 80
North Sea, 74
Norwegian Sea, 231
Nova Scotia, 118
nullipore, 28
Nurse-hound, 234

Oceanographic Institute, 229
Ocean Point, 144, 165, 171

octopus, 207
  brooding eggs, 211
  eating habits, 210
  intelligence, 212
  size, 209
Old Man Island, 183
"Oliver," 212
Ordovician period, 243
Overseas Highway, 2
oyster, 85
  California, 92
  drill, 91
  farming, 88
  feeding mechanism, 86
  Parks, 89
  spat, 87
  Virginia, 87, 91

Pacific Grove, 187, 210
Pacific Ocean, 10
Palolo worm, 30
Pamlico Sound, 77, 81
parrot fish, 51
Passion Flower, 77
pea-crab, 132
pearl fish, 53
peeler crab, 95
Pekinese Island, 142
pelican, 3, 37
Penobscot Bay, 186
periwinkle, 127, 136
  rough, 127, 129
  smooth, 128
Peru Islands, 182
petrel, 185
Philadelphia, 46
piddock, 152, 153
Pilgrims, 65

pipefish, 119
Pisaster, 190
pistol crab, 59, 63
plague, 116
plaice, 159
Pleasant Bay, 71
Pliny, 18
Plymouth, 101
pogy, 237, 239
Point Lobos, 193
Ponce de Leon, 8
Pontius Pilate, 77
porpoise, 176
Port Henderson, 37
Portuguese man-of-war, 15
prawn, 147
Pribiloff Islands, 217
Pterophryne, 5
Pzribram, Professor, 60

quahog, 97, 100, 105

red feed, 224, 225
"red water," 116
reef, 29
Remora, 17
Rhode Island, 16
Ricketts, E. K., 187
Roscoff, 110

Salcombe, 139
Samoa, 30, 31
sand dab, 158
sand dollar, 67, 68
San Francisco Bay, 75, 92
Santa Barbara, 187
sardines, 224
Sargartia troglodytes, 170

Sargasso fish, 5
Sargasso weed, 5, 6, 123
scales, herring, 225
scallop, 119, 172
　eyes, 173
　swimming, 174
sculpin, 239, 240
sea biscuit, 67
sea, cucumber, 53, 147
　fan, 28
　hare, 27
　horse, 5, 119
　lettuce, 120
　lily, 26, 244
　lion, 193
　mat, 150, 243
　otter, 193
　palm, 188
　pasture, 123
　peach, 174
　potato, 174, 175
　raven, 239
　rod, 28
　slug, 5, 150
　squirt, 66, 174
　urchin, 26, 146, 194
seal, 195, 214
　baby, 216
　hair, 217
　harbor, 217
　weaning, 219
Sesuvium, 20
shark, 48, 235
　sucker, 17
Shaw, George Bernard, 15
Sheepscot River, 172
shipworm, 151

shrimp, 158, 228, 229
　skeleton, 156
Silurian, 26
Smithsonian Institute, 33
Snail, Band, 103
snail, moon, 98
snapper, gray, 45, 46
sole, 159
sooty tern, 19, 20, 37
South Pacific, 5, 39
Spanish-American War, 36
Spanish Main, 77
Speed, John, 10
spermatophore, 204
Spice Islands, 73
spiral worm (Spirorbis), 129
sponge, boring, 151
　crab, 93
　Crumb-o'-bread, 144
　disease, 117
　farming, 62
　inhabitants, 60, 63
　regeneration, 61, 62
squid, 195
　eggs, 196
　embryo, 206
　eye, 200
　jet-propulsion, 198
　spawning, 203, 204
Stanford University, 187
starfish, 145, 189
Steinbeck, John, 187
St. Lawrence River, 243
St. Louis, 214
stone fish, 26
Straits of Florida, 4
sun star, 175

surf clam, 102
Synapta, 26

Tangalla, 13
Taranto, 68
Tarpon Springs, 62
Teredo, 153, 154
Tethys, Sea of, 74
Texas, 222
"The Toilers of the Sea," 207
tides, 164
tiger shark, 14
Tortugas (see Dry Tortugas), 2, 6
Triassic period, 74
Trilobite, 70
Tropic of Cancer, 35
Tubularia, 155
tumor, malignant, 46
tunicate, 1, 66, 174
  golden-star, 150
turtle, 3
  ancestry, 14
  coupling, 10
  eggs, 8
  food, 15
  grass, 22
  growth, 16
  hatching, 9
  hunting, 17
  nest, 7
  nest-making, 12
  tears, 11

ultra-violet light, 205
University of London, 212
University of North Carolina, 66

Vancouver, Captain, 191
Vienna, 60
Virginia, 237
Virginia Capes, 95
Virginia Company, 10
Virginia, Cull Law, 88
Virginians, 65

Walcheren Island, 131
Wallace, 140
Waymouth, Lord, 108
Weber, Max, 78
West Indies, 126
whale, 228
  shark, 229
whalebone, 228
wharf piles, 155
white heron, 2
White Sea, 226
Wilson, H. V., 60
Winthrop, John, 101
Woods Hole, 3, 229
worm, spawning, 32, 33, 34
Wrack, Bladder, 125
  Channeled, 124
  Flat, 124
  Knotted, 125
  Toothed, 125

Young, J. Z., 211
Yucatan, 2, 72

Zoea, 93, 94
Zostera, 117, 119

THIS BOOK TO BE RETURNED BY: